A LESSON FOR EVERY DAY

7–8 YEARS

LITERACY

A & C Black • London

Published 2010 by A & C Black Publishers Limited
36 Soho Square, London W1D 3QY
www.acblack.com
ISBN 978-1-4081-2539-7
Copyright text © Christine Moorcroft 2010
Editors: Dodi Beardshaw, Jane Klima, Marie Lister, Clare Robertson, Lynne Williamson
Compiled by Mary Nathan and Fakenham Photosetting

The authors and publishers would like to thank Ray Barker, Fleur Lawrence and Rifat Siddiqui for their advice in
producing this series of books.

The publishers are grateful for permission to reproduce the following:
p.35 Extract from the Ten Tales of Shellover by Ruth Ainsworth (Andre Deutsch), reproduced by permission
of Carlton Books; p. 62 Extract from The Battle of Bubble and Squeak by Philippa Pearce, text copyright ©
Philippa Pearce 1978, published by Andre Deutsch, reproduced with the permission of Scholastic Ltd, all rights
reserved; p.178: 'The Train', reproduced by permission of David Higham Associates on behalf of Clive Sansom;
p.199 'Louder!' reproduced by kind permission of the author, Roger Stevens. Every effort has been made to trace
copyright holders and obtain their permission for use of copyright material. The publishers would be pleased to
rectify any error or omission in future editions.

Printed and bound in Great Britain by Martins the Printers, Berwick-on-Tweed.

A & C Black uses paper produced with elemental chlorine-free pulp, harvested from managed sustainable forests.

Contents

Introduction

Introduction

A Lesson for Every Day: Literacy is a series of seven photocopiable activity books for developing children's ability to communicate with others through speaking and listening, and reading and writing.

The activities provide opportunities for children to read different genres, and to read fluently through using phonic knowledge of grapheme-phoneme correspondences and blending as their prime approach for decoding unfamiliar words. The books also help children to spell words accurately by combining the use of grapheme–phoneme correspondence knowledge as the prime approach, and morphological knowledge and etymological information.

The series develops children's understanding of sentences and their ability to form sentences, with activities that help them to practise their skills in organising and writing texts for different purposes.

The importance of dance, songs and rhymes is recognised in the development of communication skills. The activities provide or are linked to various games, rhymes, songs and stories as well as to familiar or everyday situations.

The books provide learning activities to support all the strands of the Primary Framework for Literacy.

The activities

To help teachers to select appropriate learning experiences for their pupils, the activities have been grouped into sections by text-type (narrative, non-fiction or poetry) and by genre. However, the activities need not be presented to children in the order in which they appear in the book, unless otherwise stated.

Some of the activities can be carried out with the whole class, some are more suitable for small groups and others

are for individual work, especially where the teacher and teaching assistants are working more closely with other groups. Many are generic and can be adapted; the notes on the activities in the grids on pages 6-24 and, in some cases, the notes at the foot of the page provide suggestions and ideas for this and for developing extension activities. Many of the activities can be adapted for use at different levels, to suit the differing levels of attainment of the children (see the teachers' notes on the pages). The activities can be used in connection with different areas of the curriculum, some of which are suggested in the notes on the activities.

The activities emphasise the importance of providing opportunities for children to enjoy novels, stories, plays, films and poetry – not just to learn about how they are written – and that children have time to listen to, repeat, learn, recite and join in poems for enjoyment. It is also important to encourage children to read non-fiction for enjoyment as well as for finding specific information.

Reading

Most children will be able to carry out the activities independently but some may need help in reading the instructions on the sheets. It is expected that someone will read them to or with them, since children learn to recognise the purpose of instructions before they can read them.

Organisation

The activities require very few resources besides pencils, crayons, scissors and glue. Other materials are specified in the teachers' notes on the pages: for example, story books, nursery rhymes, an interactive whiteboard, audio or video recording equipment (such as a tape recorder, camera or mobile phone) soft toys, dressing-up items, information books and dictionaries.

Extension activities

Most of the activity sheets end with a challenge (**Now try this!**) which reinforces and extends the children's learning. These more challenging activities might be appropriate for only a few children; it is not expected that the whole class should complete them, although many more children might benefit from them with appropriate assistance – possibly as a guided or shared activity. On some pages there is space for the children to complete extension activities that involve writing or drawing, but others will require a separate sheet of paper.

Notes on the activities

The notes on the activities in the grids on pages 6-24 expand upon those which are provided at the bottom of most activity pages. They give ideas and suggestions for making the most of the activity sheet, including suggestions for the whole-class introduction, the plenary session or for follow-up work using an adapted version of the activity sheet.

Assessment

Use the completed activities as part of your day-to-day assessment to help you to build a picture of children's learning in order to plan future teaching and learning. Activities can also be used as examples of significant evidence for your periodic assessment. In order to help you to make reliable judgements about your pupils' attainment, the assessment focuses for each activity are given in the grids on pages 6-24. Some of the activities provide opportunities for children to carry out self assessment.

Encourage children to reflect on their learning and discuss with them whether there are areas that they feel they need to practise further.

The CD-ROM

All activity sheets can be found as PDF and Word versions on the accompanying CD-ROM. These can be printed or displayed on an interactive whiteboard. The Word versions can be customised in Microsoft Word in order to assist personalised learning.

They can be accessed through an interface that makes it easy to select worksheets and display them. You can also search for lessons that will meet a particular Assessment Focus for Assessing Pupils' Progress. For more information on system requirements, please see the inside front cover.

If you have any questions regarding the *A Lesson For Every Day* CD-ROM, please email us at the address below. We will get back to you as soon as possible.

educationalsales@acblack.com

Year 3 Narrative, plays and scripts: Unit 1 Stories with familiar settings

Activity name	Strand and learning objectives	Notes on the activities	Assessment Focus	Page number
Ban the gum?	**1. Speaking** Sustain conversation, explain or give reasons for their views or choices	**Ban the gum?** is about presenting one's views to others and giving reasons for them. The children could work individually, making notes on their ideas about whether or not chewing gum should be banned and why; or the page could be completed as a group activity with each child saying what he or she thinks, while the others take turns to make notes. Ask the children to read this page and then give them time to think about the idea of banning chewing gum before they talk about it – for this they might not need a paper copy – they could read from the interactive whiteboard. **Vocabulary:** *ban, consider, explain, listen, opinion, points, reasons, view.*	**Speaking and listening AF2** Listen and respond to others, including in pairs and groups, shaping meanings through suggestions, comments, and questions	25
Pocket money: 1 and 2 Mystery tree Memory tree Character chat	**2. Listening and responding** Follow up others' points and show whether they agree or disagree in whole-class discussion	**Pocket money: 2** provides information to help the children to formulate their own views on pocket money; to listen to one another's views and then to make up their minds about what they think. You could model how to ask questions in order to find out more about what someone thinks: for example, 'Children aged eight should have £5 a week pocket money' ('If they had that much what would they use it for?'). Parents should be made to give us pocket money' ('How might they feel about that?' or 'What if they can't afford it?'). It can be used with page 26 once the children have had time to think about their opinions. **Vocabulary:** *afford, buy, earn, income, pocket money, sell, spend.* **Mystery story** is about listening to one another's ideas about a story and expressing agreement or disagreement, with reasons. This could be used as a starting point for an activity to develop skills in creating and shaping texts. So that the children can encourage others to speak you could ask each child who speaks to nominate the next speaker. Remind them that everyone should have the chance to talk about their idea and the others should listen. The spider chart should show all the ideas. The children could discuss these ideas and then decide which one is the most promising for a story. Alternatively, the children could continue the story in their groups and then tell the story to another group. **Vocabulary:** *beginning, character, ending, event, main character, message, mystery, problem, spider chart, surprise.* **Memory tree** and **Character chat** support the children in sharing memories about a story they have read, including expressing agreement or disagreement and the reasons. It also encourages them to listen carefully to one another's ideas so that they do not merely repeat them. Help the children to choose a story to which they have all had a similar level of exposure. You could model ways of developing ideas through agreement or disagreement: I remember that too, and I remember .... I thought that .... My memory of that part of the story is different. I thought that character was brave because .... I think she was clever because ... During the plenary session it is useful to draw together all the children's memories and ask them to talk about any parts of the story or any of the character's action they had forgotten but which listening to others helped them to remember. **Vocabulary:** *memory, remember, share.*	**Speaking and listening AF2** Listen and respond to others, including in pairs and groups, shaping meanings through suggestions, comments, and questions	26–27 28 29–30
Pass it on	**4. Drama** Use some drama strategies to explore stories or issues	**Pass it on** can be used to support work in citizenship (taking part in a community) and in assemblies (friendship and community). **Vocabulary:** *community, emotion, expression, feeling, influence, issue, verse.*	**Speaking and listening AF3** Create and sustain different roles and scenarios, adapting techniques in a range of dramatic activities to explore texts, ideas, and issues	31
The sea: 1 and 2	**7. Understanding and interpreting texts** Explore how different texts appeal to readers using varied sentence structures and descriptive language	**The sea: 1 and 2** are about the ways in which the atmosphere in the same setting can change and how the author creates these effects. You could explore how the writer uses sentence structure and descriptive language in describing the setting of this story. Note that she uses long sentences and asks the children how she uses punctuation to help to make the meaning clear and to help the reader to read them. Draw attention to the commas. Also point out examples of descriptive language and ask the children what these make them 'see': 'purple shadows hovered', 'curling plumes of white foam', 'a pathway on the water', 'points of light', 'jagged splinters of rock', 'fluttered like flags of white foam', 'tossed their treasures of seaweed and shells'. The passages are from *The Fairy Ship* by Alison Uttley (from *John Barleycorn*, Jonathan Cape). On a simple level the children could notice the changes in the sea at different times of the day and in different seasons. A different atmosphere is created in each passage: in the first it seems calm but a sense of threat is created by the inclusion of 'purple shadows'; the second passage has a more choppy sea, but the atmosphere is fresh and pleasant; the third passage is more mysterious with its flickering light; the fourth has a hint of impending disaster with its 'cruel waves' and 'jagged splinters of rock'; the final passage exudes calm and peace with its gentle vocabulary: *fluttered, danced, peace, goodwill.* Point out that authors can use descriptions of a setting to set the mood of part of a story and to suggest what might happen. Ask the children about the kind of event that might happen. Will it be surprising, dangerous, calm? Will it lead to something funny, an adventure or something sad?	**Reading AF2** Understand, describe, select or retrieve information, events or ideas from texts and use quotation and reference to text **Reading AF3** Deduce, infer or interpret information, events or ideas from texts **Reading AF1** Use a range of strategies including accurate decoding of text, to read for meaning **Reading AF4** Identify and comment on the structure and organisation of texts, including grammatical and presentational features at text level **Reading AF5** Explain and comment on writers' uses of language, including grammatical and literary features at word and sentence level	32–33
Settings match The flood The woods	**8. Engaging with and responding to texts** Identify features that writers use to provoke readers reactions	**Settings match** helps the children to consider the way in which an image suggests what might happen in a story. They could also look at images of settings from television plays or films and say what might happen there and what type of character might be involved. **The flood** is set in a familiar place: a garden shed. It is from *The Ten Tales of Shellover* by Ruth Ainsworth (André Deutsch). The change in mood is created by changes in the setting. Encourage them to say why they think their re-ordered passages are correct. They can describe the cat's feelings in each passage, giving evidence from the text. Point out how the author creates a feeling of growing unease or fear. The description of the setting is mirrored by the changes in the mother cat's thoughts. You could explore how the writer uses sentence structure and descriptive language in describing the setting of this story. Note that she uses some long and some short sentences. Point out examples of descriptive language, including comparisons, and ask the children what these make them see or hear: 'a great blast of wind', 'eyes shone like green lamps', 'curled like furry balls', 'zig zag flashes'. The children could underline words that help to create the changing atmosphere and communicate changes in the cat's feelings, beginning with peace and comfort and changing to wariness and caution, then fear and readiness for flight, then fear. **The woods** encourages the children to consider how changes in the same setting can suggest different atmospheres. You could display the page on an interactive whiteboard and let the children add colour to each setting to create different effects.	All Reading AFs, especially: **Reading AF6** Identify and comment on writers' purposes and viewpoints and the overall effect of the text on the reader **Reading AF3** Deduce, infer or interpret information, events or ideas from texts **Reading AF7** Relate texts to their social, cultural and historical contexts and literary traditions	34 35 36

Activity name	Strand and learning objectives	Notes on the activities	Assessment Focus	Page number
Exploring a setting Atmospheric: 1, 2 and 3	**9. Creating and shaping texts** Select and use a range of technical and descriptive vocabulary	**Exploring a setting** provides a starting point (in the form of a setting) for a story. It is useful to encourage the children to explore the setting as if they are Emil. It develops their skills in using visual elements to help them to write sentences that describe a setting and suggest what might happen in it. Ask them where he might be, where he might have come from and how he feels when he enters the house. To help them to find and use varied vocabulary, the children could make a chart for the five senses and note useful words under each heading: sight, hearing, smell, taste, touch. They could go on to describe the rest of the kitchen orally to a partner before continuing the story. Ask them to include description in their story and give other examples of sentences, modelled on those in the passage. **Atmospheric: 1, 2 and 3** help the children to develop a story set in a familiar setting. **Atmospheric: 1** provides two pictures of the same setting, which the children are asked to colour, alter and annotate to create two different atmospheres. It encourages them to use visual elements, such as layout and illustrations, to create a setting with a specific atmosphere. You could also ask them to change colour, brightness and other effects to alter a photograph displayed on a computer to create different atmospheres. They could add words to the resulting pictures to evoke the atmosphere. **Atmospheric: 2** develops their ability to structure stories (beginning, middle and ending) and to develop this structure (opening, something happens, the problem is sorted out, ending). Their ideas for the stories should develop from each setting. **Atmospheric: 3** focuses on the choice of descriptive vocabulary. The children select appropriate words for each setting from a word-bank. They could also add words of their own.	All Writing AFs, especially: **Writing AF1** Write imaginative, interesting and thoughtful texts **Writing AF2** Produce texts which are appropriate to task, reader and purpose **Writing AF7** Select appropriate and effective vocabulary	37 38–40
Words for describing Describe and draw	**11. Sentence structure and punctuation** Compose sentences using adjectives, verbs and nouns for precision, clarity and impact	**Words for describing** reinforces the children's learning about adjectives by focusing on the nouns they describe. It develops the children's understanding that there are different types of words and that they are used for different purposes in sentences. This page could be linked with the discussion of characters and settings of stories. **Describe and draw** reinforces the children's learning about adjectives by asking them to choose adjectives to describe nouns in captions. They could also be given a treasure hunt in which they have to find objects to match descriptions, such as long and green, brown and crisp, soft and black, warm and golden.	**Writing AF5** Vary sentences for clarity, purpose and effect **Writing AF6** Write with technical accuracy of syntax and punctuation in phrases, clauses and sentences	41 42

Year 3 Narrative, plays and scripts: Unit 2 Myths and legends

Activity name	Strand and learning objectives	Notes on the activities	Assessment Focus	Page number
Jack and Jill: 1–4	**3. Group discussion and interaction** Use discussion to organise roles and action	**Jack and Jill: 1, 2, 3 and 4** encourage the children to use talk to organise roles and action and to use the language of possibility to investigate and reflect on feelings, behaviour and relationships. After reading and enjoying the poem individually (or with a partner, if this helps with reading) the children could have a short unstructured discussion about it with a partner. You might need to explain some words (see Vocabulary below). Ask them how Jack felt at the end of the poem. Was he right? This is an opportunity to link with work in citizenship on relationships and conflict. You could discuss what can make it difficult for people to resolve conflicts and disagreements. Using page 43, they can organise their ideas after reading the sample notes (point out that there is no problem with disagreeing as long as the people who disagree are polite and consider one another's opinions and feelings). They can then consider how Jack and Jill could have handled their disagreement better: for example, Jack could have said what he liked about bright colours and why they were suitable for painting a picture in that place on that day; Jill could have explained why she preferred duller colours and in what way they would improve the painting. They could have agreed to paint two different types of painting on different days. Or one of them might have been able to persuade the other. On page 45 the children write complete sentences to include in a voicemail message to explain this to Jack and Jill. You could use this to consolidate work in sentence structure and punctuation. The final activity in this series of four encourages the children to write their own version of the poem, in which Jack and Jill disagree in a more friendly way; the children could enact the story and then plan the outcome together in groups. This would fit in with work on understanding and responding to texts, text structure and organisation or creating and shaping texts. **Vocabulary:** agree, disagree, clouted, consideration, cowed, crown, feelings, impolite, listen, polite, right, rude, views, wrong.	**Speaking and listening AF2** Listen and respond to others, including in pairs and groups, shaping meanings through suggestions, comments, and questions	43–46
Windy nights: 1 & 2	**3. Group discussion and interaction** Actively include and respond to all members of the group	**Windy Nights: 1 and 2** encourage the children to use talk to organise roles and action and to use the language of possibility to investigate and reflect on feelings. The activities can be used in conjunction with work on understanding and responding to texts. In order to increase the volume, more and more children could join in the reading, and then to decrease the volume they could drop out one by one. In addition to this they can make their voices progressively louder and then quieter, having decided just how loud and how quiet is appropriate. interest/important points as 'buzz' suggests conversation. **Vocabulary:** buzz point, discuss, gallop, listen, share.	**Speaking and listening AF2** Listen and respond to others, including in pairs and groups, shaping meanings through suggestions, comments, and questions	47–48

Activity name	Strand and learning objectives	Notes on the activities	Assessment Focus	Page number
Persephone and the seasons	**8. Engaging with and responding to texts** Identify features that writers use to provoke readers reactions	**Persephone and the seasons** helps the children to trace the course of the main events of a quest myth. It is based on the well-known Greek myth about Hades, the god of the Underworld who snatches Persephone and takes her to the Underworld to be his wife. Tell the children the story or let them read it for themselves. A brief outline of the story is given here. You could discuss story structure more generally, so that children become aware that the Midas and Persephone stories are both stories that are shaped by problems and their solutions. Demeter was the goddess of crops and seasons. She had a beautiful daughter named Persephone. Hades, the god of the Underworld (the land of the dead), wanted to marry Persephone. One day when Persephone was out in a meadow with her friends the water nymphs, Hades came along in his chariot and kidnapped her and took her into the Underworld. As soon Demeter realised that Persephone was missing, she began to search for her. She said that while her daughter was missing no plants would grow. Weeks went by and nothing grew on earth. People started to complain to Zeus, the king of the gods. Eventually he said that Persephone could come back. However, Hades reminded Zeus that there was a rule that anyone who had eaten in the Underworld was not allowed out. Zeus asked Persephone if she had eaten in the Underworld. A hush fell on all the gods. They all looked at Persephone. Persephone looked at Demeter and at Zeus and said, "I ate six pomegranate seeds." But Zeus took pity on Demeter and Persephone and ruled that time all the plants would stop that she must spend part of each year in the Underworld. Demeter said that during that time all the plants stopped growing – that was winter. So, every year, as soon as Persephone went back to the Underworld the plants stopped growing – that was winter.	All Reading AFs, especially: **Reading AF6** Identify and comment on writers' purposes and viewpoints and the overall effect of the text on the reader **Reading AF3** Deduce, infer or interpret information, events or ideas from texts **Reading AF7** Relate texts to their social, cultural and historical contexts and literary traditions	49
The quest		**The quest** can be used to help the children to consider features of quest myths in general: changes of setting during the quest, dangers facing the main character and ways in which he or she keeps safe. Examples of published quest myths include: *A First Myths Storybook* by Mary Hoffman (Dorling Kindersley), *The Iron Man* by Ted Hughes (Faber), *The Orchard Book of Greek Myths* by Geraldine McCaughrean (Orchard), *Perseus and the Gorgon Medusa* by Geraldine McCaughrean (Orchard), *Theseus and the Minotaur* by Geraldine McCaughrean (Orchard), *The Adventures of Odysseus* by Geraldine McCaughrean (Orchard), *Jason and the Golden Fleece* by Geraldine McCaughrean (Orchard), *The Twelve Labours of Heracles* by Geraldine McCaughrean (Orchard), *Rama and the Demon King* by Jessica Souhami (Frances Lincoln).		50
Character and quest	**10. Text structure and organisation** Signal sequence, place and time to give coherence	**Character and quest**, **Quest game** and **Quest cards** are about planning a quest myth. It helps if the children decide on a character and a purpose for the quest using what they have learned from quest myths they have read. **Character and quest** focuses on the character and the ultimate purpose of the quest. **Quest game**, accompanied by **Quest cards**, helps to generate ideas about challenges the character might meet during the quest and about objects and other characters that might help or harm him or her. After playing the game ask the children to make a note of the characters, events, places and objects they encountered. You could ask questions (or let the children ask one another questions) about what happened to their main character in a particular setting, the problem it caused and how the character overcame it (also how he or she was helped by another character, an animal or an object, as appropriate). Ask the children to consider whether the character changed during the quest: for example, becoming braver, wiser or happier. They could make notes about, and enact, some of their ideas. Also encourage them to make up their own objects and settings. These could involve magic, spells, folklore, passwords and other elements the children come across in their reading. **Quest route** is about signalling sequence in a story. It helps the children to plan a quest myth with events located in specific settings. It could be used with pages 51–53 or to create a new story. The children should imagine their character travelling through the scene and make notes about what happens in three of the locations in the picture. Help them to convert their notes into sentences and to use connectives to sequence them. **The Chest of Promises** focuses on the purpose of a quest (to find the Chest of Promises). The children could first discuss or enact the scene where their character finds the Chest of Promises: where it is located, including the difficulties involved in accessing this place; how the character finds it; how it is protected (electronically, by means of traditional devices or by guards such as monsters, ogres or robots); and how the character defeats these. You could make an ornate 'chest of promises' from a decorated cardboard box and write some promises on scrolls of paper tied with ribbons: for example, 'The guardian of the forest promises to protect you from all harm', 'The spirits of lost children promise to show you the way to the treasure', 'The Ghost of Doom promises not to harm you if you keep travelling towards the morning sun'.	**Writing AF3** Organise and present whole texts effectively, sequencing and structuring information, ideas and events **Writing AF4** Construct paragraphs and use cohesion within and between paragraphs	51–53
Quest game				
Quest cards				
Quest route				54
The Chest of Promises				55

Activity name	Strand and learning objectives	Notes on the activities	Assessment Focus	Page number
On your screen	**11. Sentence structure and punctuation** Show relationships of time, reason and cause, through subordination and connectives	**On your screen** reinforces the children's understanding of a sentence. They are required to identify the ends of sentences and the beginnings of new ones and to demarcate them using capital letters and full stops. It is useful to point out that punctuation is a useful tool which helps children to write what they mean and for others to understand what they mean. In addition to using the page as directed, on another copy you could also insert full stops, commas and capital letters in the wrong places and ask the children to read the passage, for example: The wind became. Stronger it was, blowing. Me, back, but I had to reach. The other side of the beach sprays. Of sand dashed onto my. Face, I kept my mouth, tightly. Closed, my eyes hurt. There was sand in my mouth, then my foot. Struck something. Hard, it felt. Like metal. Discuss the changes in meaning. This and other passages from stories could be scanned and displayed on an interactive whiteboard. Using a split screen, you could display the undifferentiated and the corrected versions simultaneously for comparison.	**Writing AF5** Vary sentences for clarity, purpose and effect **Writing AF6** Write with technical accuracy of syntax and punctuation in phrases, clauses and sentences	56
Past and present: 1 and 2		**Past and present: 1** and **2** reinforce the children's understanding of the past and present tenses. It can be linked with word-level work on adding suffixes to form the past tense and on irregular verbs in which a different word is used for the past tense or when the spelling remains the same but the pronunciation changes (for example, *read*). **Past and present: 1** is concerned with the simple present and past tenses: *walk/walked, say/said, do/did, run/ran* and so on. **Past and present: 2** focuses on the present and past tense formed with auxiliary verbs: *am/are/is/was/were; walking, saying, doing, running* and so on. Link this with work on spelling – adding the suffixes *-ed* and *-ing* and changing the ending of the root word where necessary (doubling the final consonant, dropping the final *e*).		57–58
One thing after another		**One thing after another** develops the children's understanding about how words are used in recounts to show the order in which events happen. They could also create a personal word-bank of useful words to use in stories for showing when things happen. As a further extension activity, you could ask the children to add information to simple sentences such as *Rani bought an ice cream.* Type up the sentences, display them on an interactive whiteboard and make copies for the children to alter in different ways. Ask them to add words that say when, how and where (and even why).		59
Because		**Because** develops the children's understanding of the purposes of connectives. Introduce the term connective and point out that connectives can show when, where, how or why something happened. Ask them about words they have used for joining sentences, including *because*. Can the children spell *because*? This could be linked with the challenge to take out the word *because* and split the sentences into two shorter ones. This could be linked with the writing of instructions – adding an explanation: for example, *Do not bake for too long as this can lead to a bitter taste.*		60
That's why		**That's why** develops the children's understanding of the purposes of connectives. Remind them of the connectives they have used (because and point out that connectives which show purposes. Tell them that they are going to use some other connectives which show purposes – what someone does something for. Ask them to read the words on the word-bank and to notice that one of the connectives is made up of three words (*in order to*). Ask them to choose the best connective to help them to add a purpose to each sentence.		61

Year 3 Narrative, plays and scripts: Unit 3 Adventure and mystery

Activity name	Strand and learning objectives	Notes on the activities	Assessment Focus	Page number
A noise in the night: 1 and 2	**3. Group discussion and interaction** Use the language of possibility to investigate and reflect on feelings, behaviour or relationships	**A noise in the night: 1** and **2** focus on preparing a story for performance. You could use the story to introduce onomatopoeia: *creak* and *whispered*. It is useful to cover the passage except for the first sentence. Ask the children to read this to themselves and to imagine the scene. Ask what they would see and hear and, as they tell you, model how to use their voices to make their words sound like their meanings: *quiet, silent, breathing*. It is useful to model how to read on in a similar way: expressive words include *creak, stirred, groaned, whispered, listen*. In practice, making notes or marks on the text itself would be the most user-friendly way of preparing for a performance. Some children could experiment with their own way of doing this. **Vocabulary:** *atmosphere, character, expression, loud, mood, narrator, pitch, quiet, sound effects, tone, voice, volume.*	**Speaking and listening AF1** Talk in purposeful and imaginative ways to explore ideas and feelings, adapting and varying structure and vocabulary according to purpose, listeners, and content	62–63
Abraham and Sarah	**4. Drama** Use some drama strategies to explore stories or issues	**Abraham and Sarah.** After reading the passage, discuss the possible responses of Abraham: sadness at the idea of leaving his home and family, or pride and honour at having been chosen to be the father of a great nation. Then talk about how Sarah might have felt. **Vocabulary:** *act, dialogue, faith, feelings, respond, response, scene.*	**Speaking and listening AF3** Create and sustain different roles and scenarios, adapting techniques in a range of dramatic activities to explore texts, ideas, and issues	64

Activity name	Strand and learning objectives	Notes on the activities	Assessment Focus	Page number
Adventure peak	**7. Understanding and interpreting texts** Explore how different texts appeal to readers using varied sentence structures and descriptive language	**Adventure peak** helps the children to identify the most important event in a story and to record the events that lead up to, and follow, this event. Some stories might have more than two events leading up to the main event and perhaps one afterwards; for these you would need a different mountain shape. After completing this page the children could draw story mountains in the appropriate shapes for other stories and record the main events on them.	**Reading AF2** Understand, describe, select or retrieve information, events or ideas from texts and use quotation and reference to text	65
The search		**The search** helps the children to focus on a common story theme – a search (for a person, object or place). The activity provides support to help the children to track the main character's search by listing the settings. They could also note what happens in each setting and notice the chapter structure: each new setting might begin with a new chapter. Published examples of stories to use with this activity include: *One Hundred and One Dalmatians* by Dodie Smith (Puffin), *The Story of Persephone* (various sources), *Bye Bye Baby* by Janet & Allan Ahlberg (Puffin).	**Reading AF3** Deduce, infer or interpret information, events or ideas from texts **Reading AF1** Use a range of strategies including accurate decoding of text, to read for meaning **Reading AF4** Identify and comment on the structure and organisation of texts, including grammatical and presentational features at text level **Reading AF5** Explain and comment on writers' uses of language, including grammatical and literary features at word and sentence level	66
Wrong to right	**8. Engaging with and responding to texts** Empathise with characters and debate moral dilemmas portrayed in texts	**Wrong to right** helps the children to focus on a common story theme – putting right a wrong which has been committed. The activity provides support to help the children to identify the wrong and what the character tries to do; also to identify factors that might make this difficult and how they might be overcome. There are opportunities for links with work in Citizenship on right and wrong. Published examples of stories to use with this activity include: *The Twelve Labours of Heracles* by Geraldine McCaughrean (Orchard), *The Story of Persephone* (various sources), *Charlotte's Web* by E B White (Puffin), *Colm of the Islands* by Rosemary Harris (Walker), *Jo-Jo's Journey* by Grahame Baker-Smith (Bodley Head), *One Hundred and One Dalmatians* by Dodie Smith (Puffin).	All Reading AFs, especially: **Reading AF6** Identify and comment on writers' purposes and viewpoints and the overall effect of the text on the reader **Reading AF3** Deduce, infer or interpret information, events or ideas from texts **Reading AF7** Relate texts to their social, cultural and historical contexts and literary traditions	67
In the hot seat		**In the hot seat** provides a format to help the children to prepare for a 'hot-seating' session in which one of them takes the part of the main character in a story and the others ask questions. Focus on questions which ask why the character did various actions.		68
Clues	**8. Engaging with and responding to texts** Identify features that writers use to provoke readers reactions	**Clues** focuses on information contained in a mystery story that gives clues about events and characters. It also introduces the idea of information the author keeps hidden from the reader until near the end but which they might be able to guess from the clues. You could also provide the children with police officers' notebooks and ask them to make notes about what has happened and to record clues that might help them to solve the mystery. They could co-operate in groups on the solution of a 'police investigation'. Published examples of stories to use with this activity include: *Fowl Play* by Jonathan Allen (Dolphin), *Betsey Biggalow the Detective* by Malorie Blackman (Mammoth), *Julian, Secret Agent* by Ann Cameron (Corgi, Yearling), *Private Eye of New York* by Nigel Gray (Mammoth), *Chocolate Money Mystery* by Alexander McCall Smith (Scholastic), *The Secret of Weeping Wood* by Robert Swindells (Hippo).	All Reading AFs, especially: **Reading AF6** Identify and comment on writers' purposes and viewpoints and the overall effect of the text on the reader **Reading AF3** Deduce, infer or interpret information, events or ideas from texts **Reading AF7** Relate texts to their social, cultural and historical contexts and literary traditions	69
The Castle Site discovery	**9. Creating and shaping texts** Make decisions about form and purpose, identify success criteria and use them to evaluate their own writing	**The Castle Site discovery** helps the children to create a logical structure and to sequence events in a story. It is based on a story setting from page 72 and provides questions to help the children to build up suspense in their stories. It is useful first to discuss the effect they want to create and how much of the mystery they want to reveal to the reader. Encourage them to write some short and some longer sentences to help to create interest. They could use this page for trying out ideas that could then be edited and improved in the final story.	All Writing AFs, especially: **Writing AF1** Write imaginative, interesting and thoughtful texts **Writing AF2** Produce texts which are appropriate to task, reader and purpose **Writing AF7** Select appropriate and effective vocabulary	70
Mystery story starter cards	**9. Creating and shaping texts** Use beginning, middle and end to write narratives in which events are sequenced logically and conflicts resolved	**Mystery story starter cards** provides starting points for mystery stories. Once the children have had time to think about the scene and what might happen they could begin to plan a story, possibly beginning with a hot-seating activity (see page 69).	All Writing AFs, especially: **Writing AF1** Write imaginative, interesting and thoughtful texts	71
The Thought Stone hot seat		**The Thought Stone hot seat** helps the children to develop their idea for a story, using a starting point from page 72. Encourage them to say what the 'Thought Stone' is, what they will let the reader know at the start of the story and what they will reveal later – or at the end. The questions on this page could be masked and replaced with new ones to help to develop a different story.	**Writing AF2** Produce texts which are appropriate to task, reader and purpose **Writing AF7** Select appropriate and effective vocabulary	72
The Always Silk Scarf story mountain		**The Always Silk Scarf story mountain** helps the children to structure a narrative using beginning, middle and ending in a way that sequences events logically and includes the resolution of a conflict or problem. The notes they make on the flags help them to build up tension to the main event in the story and then present the aftermath so that the story does not tail off. Encourage the children to comment on one another's ideas and to suggest improvements where appropriate. You may wish to exercise caution with or even omit this page if any of the children has recently lost a grandparent.		73
A Crack in the Street dialogue	**9. Creating and shaping texts** Select and use a range of technical and descriptive vocabulary	**A Crack in the Street dialogue** helps the children to write a dialogue based on a picture and a description of a setting that tells the story and builds up the reader's interest. You could invite the children to enact a scene in which a crowd of people see a huge crack appearing in a street; how the people feel and how they express these feelings (through actions and words). When they write the dialogue encourage them to use adverbs and other verbs for 'said' to help to create the effect of shock and fear. This can be linked with sentence structure work on writing direct speech.	All Writing AFs, especially: **Writing AF1** Write imaginative, interesting and thoughtful texts **Writing AF2** Produce texts which are appropriate to task, reader and purpose **Writing AF7** Select appropriate and effective vocabulary	74

Activity name	Strand and learning objectives	Notes on the activities	Assessment Focus	Page number
Into the past	**11. Sentence structure and punctuation** Compose sentences using adjectives, verbs and nouns for precision, clarity and impact	**Into the past** helps the children to understand the purpose and use of the past and present tenses in writing. It introduces the consistent use of a tense in narrative. During the plenary session you could ask volunteers to read the passage in the present and then the past tense for comparison.	**Writing AF5** Vary sentences for clarity, purpose and effect **Writing AF6** Write with technical accuracy of syntax and punctuation in phrases, clauses and sentences	75
Time travel		**Time travel** develops skills in using tenses consistently. You could also provide speech bubble-shaped cards on which the children can write other words for the robots (choosing either the present or past tense) and then pass to a friend to check that the tense is the same throughout. These could then be mixed up and sorted into two sets: past and present.		76
Action sentences		**Action sentences** is about choosing expressive verbs for movement in order to create an impression of subjects. It provides lists of verbs and settings from which the children can choose the most appropriate. They could begin by matching the subjects to the settings and then selecting the best verb. During the plenary session discuss why they chose these verbs and the impression they create. The children could key in sentences containing verbs such as *go, say* or *had* from stories with the settings and then invite suggestions for different verbs. Display them, one at a time, on an interactive whiteboard and invite suggestions for different verbs. Discuss the effects of these verbs and choose the most expressive for the context.		77
Exclamation words	**11. Sentence structure and punctuation** Clarify meaning through the use of exclamation marks and speech marks	**Exclamation words** shows the children how to form an exclamation mark. You could point out that part of an exclamation mark is the same as a full stop because it is usually used at the end of a sentence. The part above the full stop shows that the sentence is an exclamation. Explain what this means using examples such as *Help! Come here! Go away! Stop! As a* homework activity the children could collect examples of exclamations from comic books and newspaper cartoons. This can be linked with text-level work on jokes and humour.	**Writing AF5** Vary sentences for clarity, purpose and effect **Writing AF6** Write with technical accuracy of syntax and punctuation in phrases, clauses and sentences	78
Ha, ha!		**Ha, ha!** helps the children to distinguish between sentences which are questions and others which are exclamations. This can be linked with text-level work on jokes and humour. The children could begin a class joke collection, either as a display or on a computer. Encourage them to check that the questions have question marks and the funny answers have exclamation marks.		79
Knock, knock		**End points** consolidates the children's understanding of punctuation at the ends of sentences: when to use a full stop, an exclamation mark or a question mark. You could point out that part of a question mark is the same as a full stop because it belongs at the end of a sentence. The part above the full stop shows that the sentence is a question. Also point out that part of an exclamation mark is the same as a full stop because it belongs at the end of a sentence. The part above the full stop shows that the sentence is an exclamation.		80
Story talk		**Knock, knock** provides practice in writing dialogue using speech bubbles. It reinforces the children's learning that the spoken words are enclosed in a speech bubble, preparing them for using speech marks for the same purpose in text. The children could also make a class collection of 'knock, knock' jokes, written using speech bubbles and/or speech marks.		81
If animals could talk		**Story talk** introduces speech marks for enclosing spoken words in text. The children are asked to identify the spoken words in a passage. Note that this story is printed with only single quotation marks, not double as used elsewhere. They could first practise writing speech marks. You could present the marks as 66 and 99 because the first resembles the number 66 in orientation and the second resembles the number 99. Encourage them to write the speech marks in line with the tops of the tallest letters.		82
Speech marks		**If animals could talk** is about the use of speech marks to replace speech bubbles. The children should write only the spoken words between the speech marks. You could draw attention to the other punctuation: the use of a comma at the end of spoken words followed by *said* or any other verb for *said*.		83
Speech on the page		**Speech marks** and **Speech on the page** reinforce the children's learning about dialogue and focuses on the positioning of speech marks with relation to the spoken words and the surrounding text. Point out that when the spoken words are followed by *said* or a similar word the full stop at the end of the spoken words is changed to a comma (but note that question marks and exclamation marks are retained).		84–85

Year 3 Narrative, plays and scripts: Unit 4 Authors and letters

Activity name	Strand and learning objectives	Notes on the activities	Assessment Focus	Page number
Sale	**3. Group discussion and interaction** Use discussion to organise roles and action	**Sale** presents a task that requires the children to use talk to organise actions. They should consider the reasons why the Green family should sell or keep each item. You could provide hints for them to consider, such as which items might fetch the highest prices; which they can most easily manage without; what the owners might feel about their loss; which items, if kept, might afford savings in the longer term. They could also enact a conversation in which they persuade someone who is reluctant to sell an item that its sale would help the family achieve its goal of buying and maintaining a puppy. **Vocabulary:** *cash, money, persuade, polite, sacrifice, savings.*	**Speaking and listening AF2** Listen and respond to others, including in pairs and groups, shaping meanings through suggestions, comments, and questions	86
Pairs Discussion words	**3. Group discussion and interaction** Actively include and respond to all members of the group	**Pairs** encourages the children actively to include and respond to all members of the group. Use it in connection with work in science on light and shadows. The discussion could reveal assumptions that the children make. These might not be challenged by the others; this is where adult intervention in the form of questions is useful but from the point of view of developing the children's understanding and for modelling how to challenge an assumption in a way that makes it acceptable to the person who holds the assumption. Point out the importance of questioning our own knowledge about something – we are 'sure' of. After completing the activity, the children can swap answer sheets with other groups, or two from each group could visit other groups in order to share ideas. This could lead to further discussions among the groups about the ideas offered by others. You could comment on how questions are phrased and the difference between open and closed questions. Answers: *The Sun is low in the sky* and *The shadows are long; The Sun is high in the sky* and *The shadows are short: A sundial* and *Tell the time; The mug blocks light coming from the lamp* and *A shadow is formed; The Sun looks as if it moves across the sky* and *Shadows change direction:* **Vocabulary:** *block, direction, knowledge, learning, light, question, shadow, share, sundial, time, translucent, transparent.* **Discussion words** focuses on responding to other members of the group. The children sort the cards into sets (polite and impolite words and phrases for discussions as well as words/phrases which are neither polite nor impolite, or which depend on tone of voice). They could comment on how they would feel if someone said these words or phrases to them. You could also set them a homework task – to identify polite and impolite discussion talk in (children's) television programmes they watch. **Vocabulary:** *agree, disagree, impolite, rude.*	**Speaking and listening AF2** Listen and respond to others, including in pairs and groups, shaping meanings through suggestions, comments, and questions	87 88
What if...?	**3. Group discussion and interaction** Use the language of possibility to investigate and reflect on feelings, behaviour or relationships	**What if...?** This activity develops the children's skills in using the language of possibility to investigate and reflect on feelings, behaviour or relationships. **Vocabulary:** *because, character, choice, consequence, could, if, in case, maybe, might, possibly, should, so, then, whether, why, would.*	**Speaking and listening AF1** Talk in purposeful and imaginative ways to explore ideas and feelings, adapting and varying structure and vocabulary according to purpose, listeners, and content	89
An author I like	**8. Engaging with and responding to texts** Share and compare reasons for reading preferences, extending range of books read	**An author I like** provides a format to help the children to record characters and books by an author they like, as well as what they like about his or her use of language. They could use their notes to help them to tell the others what they like about the author they chose. Afterwards, encourage the others to ask questions about the author's books, characters and language.	All Reading AFs, especially: **Reading AF6** Identify and comment on writers' purposes and viewpoints and the overall effect of the text on the reader **Reading AF3** Deduce, infer or interpret information, events or ideas from texts **Reading AF7** Relate texts to their social, cultural and historical contexts and literary traditions	90
Notes for a letter Notes to sentences A letter to an author Read this book	**9. Creating and shaping texts** Use layout, format, graphics and illustrations for different purposes	**Notes for a letter, Notes to sentences** and **A letter to an author** help the children to explore work by an author and to plan a letter to the author to find out how he or she works and what inspires the stories. They develop skills in making notes in a logical way that will help them to write sentences in a logical sequence. Grouped according to topic. You could mask the prompts on pages 92 and 94 if this is appropriate to the children's interests or level of independence. **Notes for a letter** helps them to get started by making notes about what they like about an author's work and what they would like to know. **Notes to sentences** is based on notes about *The Sheep-Pig* by Dick King-Smith (Puffin). The sequence of the notes and of the sentences the children will write based on them provides a model for the children to use for their own note-making and letter-writing. **A letter to an author** provides a format to help the children to set out a letter to an author (or to anyone else they do not know well). Introduce the 'signing-off' phrase *Yours sincerely* for letters where the recipient is addressed by name (rather than *Dear Sir* or *Dear Madam*) but is not known well by the writer. The letters could be word-processed for a class display. **Read this book** develops skills in making decisions about form and purpose as the children write another letter – this time an informal one to someone they know well. You could focus on the type of language, as well as the type of greeting and signing-off, that is appropriate for use in each type of letter: for example, the use of short forms of words and slang terms. Note also that when they write to a friend they will be able to include shared experiences and memories.	All Writing AFs, especially: **Writing AF1** Write imaginative, interesting and thoughtful texts **Writing AF2** Produce texts which are appropriate to task, reader and purpose **Writing AF7** Select appropriate and effective vocabulary	91–93 94

Activity name	Strand and learning objectives	Notes on the activities	Assessment Focus	Page number
Setting sentences	**11. Sentence structure and punctuation** Compose sentences using adjectives, verbs and nouns for precision, clarity and impact	**Setting sentences** is about choosing expressive verbs to use instead of *was*. It provides sections of sentences to describe places using expressive verbs. The children are asked to match up a building, a word for *was* and a place: for example, *Valley farm nestled in a hollow overlooking the village. Elm Street School squatted among gas works and old warehouses. Station Cottages stretched along the old railway. Priory Mews clung to the wall of the church. Rook Castle guarded the town.* The children could also try swapping the verbs, or trying new ones, to compare the effects. The children could begin a section for a class thesaurus listing verbs to replace *is/was* in sentences saying where something *is/was* situated. Help them to find examples in a range of texts, including fiction, advertisements (printed or audio), leaflets, documentary film voice-overs, information books, poems and Internet sources.	**Writing AF5** Vary sentences for clarity, purpose and effect **Writing AF6** Write with technical accuracy of syntax and punctuation in phrases, clauses and sentences	95
All change		**All change** reinforces the children's learning about adjectives by asking them to change the adjectives in captions in order to describe the objects in the pictures. It could be linked with work on persuasive texts in which the children could change unpleasant descriptive words to make something sound pleasant.		96
Verb detective		**Verb detective** reinforces the children's learning about verbs and nouns by asking them to identify the verbs in a text. It is useful to point out that some verbs denote being rather than any movement or obvious action: for example, to be, to live, to exist. This page could be linked with text-level work on myths and legends.		97
Verb sort		**Verb sort** reinforces the children's learning about verbs and nouns by asking them to sort a set of cards according to whether they are nouns or verbs and then to use them to complete a sentence. During the plenary session, invite volunteers to give sentences they can remember from the game. Draw out that sentences can say silly things but still make sense as sentences.		98

Year 3 Narrative, plays and scripts: Unit 5 Dialogue and plays

Activity name	Strand and learning objectives	Notes on the activities	Assessment Focus	Page number
Food guards	**1. Speaking** Sustain conversation, explain or give reasons for their views or choices	**Food guards.** In this activity the children find out how different foods are good for us and about any damage they can do. The activity supports work in science and citizenship (democracy and voting). Point out that the children will need to sound convincing in order to persuade their group. Model how to use your voice persuasively. **Vocabulary:** *choice, choose, convince, explain, listen, persuade, voice, vote.*	**Speaking and listening AF2** Listen and respond to others, including in pairs and groups, shaping meanings through suggestions, comments, and questions	99
Sandwich	**3. Group discussion and interaction** Use discussion to organise roles and action	**Sandwich** requires the children to talk to organise roles and action. It can be used in connection with design and technology activities on healthy snacks. Let them have time to read and think about the task before they speak to one another. After the children have completed the section on what the package must do, it is useful to ask them to identify ideas they might not have thought of if they had been working alone. Point out how working as a group can help them to learn. Ask the children how they will decide who is going to draw the group's idea and how they will ensure that everyone's ideas are considered. For the different roles in this group activity they might consider who is good at spelling or drawing, who writes neatly and quickly, who is good at practical tasks. Some children might not be happy with the allocation of tasks. It is useful to prepare them for this beforehand and remind them that their roles are all making an important contribution and that they can have different roles in group tasks in different activities. **Vocabulary:** *agree, because, consider, disagree, discuss, listen, talent.*	**Speaking and listening AF2** Listen and respond to others, including in pairs and groups, shaping meanings through suggestions, comments, and questions	100
Guess who	**4. Drama** Present events and characters through dialogue to engage the interest of an audience	**Guess who.** Ask the children to think about how they will engage the interest of their audience. You could encourage them to treat this in a humorous way. **Vocabulary:** *act, character, conversation, dialogue, role.*	**Speaking and listening AF3** Create and sustain different roles and scenarios, adapting techniques in a range of dramatic activities to explore texts, ideas, and issues	101
Digging up the past		**Digging up the past.** This kind of activity could be linked with any period being studied by the children. If a mock dig is carried out, the children could photograph their 'finds' and import their photographs into a word-processed report about them, written during a literacy lesson. **Vocabulary:** *act, answer, archaeologist, artefact, conversation, dialogue, enact, question, role-play.*		102
Lost in the woods		**Lost in the woods.** Ask the children to consider whether their character might help others or need help. Which character might become the leader of the group? How might they support one another? What would be their strengths and weaknesses? Might some act selfishly? Would any character harm the others? Allow opportunities for the children to perform their scenes. **Vocabulary:** *act, character, conversation, dialogue, drama, personality, role, scene.*		103
In the wrong		**In the wrong.** Here the children use drama techniques to explore why making the right choices is not always easy: for example, Lucy might not want to fall out with Patrick, she might be afraid to disagree with him or she might worry about doing something which she later regrets. **Vocabulary:** *act, agree, bullying, dialogue, disagree, drama, fair, friend, right, role-play, scene, unfair, wrong.*		104
Victims	**4. Drama** Use some drama strategies to explore stories or issues	**Victims.** After the children have completed the main activity, invite feedback and draw out the possible consequences for the victim, apart from the loss of their property. **Vocabulary:** *dialogue, emotions, event, feelings, issue, monologue, role, role-play.*	**Speaking and listening AF3** Create and sustain different roles and scenarios, adapting techniques in a range of dramatic activities to explore texts, ideas, and issues	105
Costume drama	**4. Drama** Identify and discuss qualities of others' performances, including gesture, action and costume	**Costume drama.** Begin by showing the children a photograph of a character from a film and asking them what his/her clothes tell them about the character. **Vocabulary:** *audience, character, clothes, costume, drama, wardrobe.*	**Speaking and listening AF4** Understand the range and uses of spoken language, commenting on meaning and impact and draw on this when talking to others	106

Activity name	Strand and learning objectives	Notes on the activities	Assessment Focus	Page number
King Midas' wish	**7. Understanding and interpreting texts** Infer characters' feelings in fiction and consequences in logical explanations	**King Midas's wish** focuses on how a story is organised. It is based on a common theme in myths and traditional tales – a wish. It encourages the children to think of the consequences of a decision made by the main character. There are opportunities for speaking and listening as they discuss why Midas's wish was foolish. They could also read other 'wish' stories: *Aladdin* (*The Thousand and One Nights*), *The Three Wishes*, *The Sausage* (traditional Swedish tale), *The Two-Headed Weaver* (*The Panchantatra*), *The Ridiculous Wishes* (Charles Perrault).	**Reading AF2** Understand, describe, select or retrieve information, events or ideas from texts and use quotation and reference to text **Reading AF3** Deduce, infer or interpret information, events or ideas from texts **Reading AF1** Use a range of strategies including accurate decoding of text, to read for meaning **Reading AF4** Identify and comment on the structure and organisation of texts, including grammatical and presentational features at text level **Reading AF5** Explain and comment on writers' uses of language, including grammatical and literary features at word and sentence level	107
Pantomime characters	**9. Creating and shaping texts** Make decisions about form and purpose, identify success criteria and use them to evaluate their own writing	**Pantomime characters** helps the children to make decisions about form and purpose as they make notes about the characters for a pantomime for younger children. They will need to refer to a copy of the story of *Cinderella* (written for their own age group). You could link this with work on traditional tales. The children could also make notes about any characters that are not listed on this page. Ask them to imagine the characters and to make notes about their appearance and personal qualities and to say whether they are good or evil, also *who* they are and their connections to other characters: for example, prince, prince's servant, Cinderella's step-sister, Cinderella's fairy godmother. You might need to explain what a godmother is, especially if the children know little about Christian baptism.	All Writing AFs, especially: **Writing AF1** Write imaginative, interesting and thoughtful texts **Writing AF2** Produce texts which are appropriate to task, reader and purpose **Writing AF7** Select appropriate and effective vocabulary	108
Pantomime dialogue: 1–3		**Pantomime dialogue: 1, 2** and **3** help the children to use layout and to make decisions about form and purpose as they write dialogue suitable for an audience of younger children. They could first enact the scenes with a partner and identify the spoken words, then decide whether they have to change them to suit their audience. They have an opportunity to develop their skills in writing dialogue sentences before converting them to play script form. Some children might be able to add stage directions to tell the characters how to speak and what to do. These could be added to the margin using a different colour. When the children have completed their play script, they could enact the dialogues in front of the younger children who are their target audience.		109–111
Television talk		**Television talk** focuses on dialogue represented in the form of a script. The children convert the script into dialogue using speech marks. It is useful to point out how the spoken words are represented on paper to show who is speaking and what they say. A useful follow-up activity would be to listen to a short television or radio interview and write what the people said. Working in pairs, the children could record the interview and then replay it, stopping to transcribe it.		112
Scriptwriter		**Scriptwriter** is about changing dialogue with speech marks into a play script. The children are required to identify the spoken words in the story and write them in play script form. As this traditional story continues, the man pulls his coat tightly around himself to keep warm in the strong wind. The sun shines so brightly that the weather becomes extremely hot and the man has to take off his coat – so the sun won the argument. They could repeat this process with other fables, since fables are usually very short. See http://www.aesopfables.com/ or http://www.pun-n-fun.org.uk/fabled/fontaine/fontaine.html. You might find it useful to copy and alter these to simplify the language. To help the children to set out playscripts, create a table in Word, with a narrow column for the names of the characters speaking and a wider column for the spoken words.		113
Dialogue to script: 1 and 2	**9. Creating and shaping texts** Use layout, format, graphics, illustrations for different purposes	**Dialogue to script: 1** and **2** develop the children's understanding of how playscripts are structured. They can be linked with sentence-level work on speech marks and dialogue. Ensure that children doing the NTT on page 115 only underline words like *dying, give*. Children doing the NTT on page 115 could write the stage directions in the space under each character's name on the left of the page. You could use an interactive whiteboard to model showing how to change one form of text into another by moving, deleting, adding script.	All Writing AFs, especially: **Writing AF1** Write imaginative, interesting and thoughtful texts **Writing AF2** Produce texts which are appropriate to task, reader and purpose **Writing AF7** Select appropriate and effective vocabulary	114–115
Growing sentences	**11. Sentence structure and punctuation** Show relationships of time, reason and cause, through subordination and connectives	**Growing sentences** develops the children's understanding of how sentences work and how to construct compound sentences. Use the completed example to model the way in which a sentence can be extended, and discuss the effect of this. Draw out that by adding to a sentence the writer can create an impression or give information. You could set a challenge for the children – to create the longest possible sentence. Draw out, however, that it is not always a good thing to write very long sentences. Sometimes short ones are more effective. A simple sentence contains one clause. A compound sentence contains more than one clause of equal value (i.e., there are no subordinate clauses): for example, *The adults were chatting and the children were playing*. A complex sentence (also called a multiple sentence) contains at least one main clause and at least one subordinate clause: for example, *The girl ate the sandwiches which her father had prepared for her*. The subordinate clause (italicised) does not make sense as a sentence. A main clause makes sense on its own as a sentence but a subordinate clause depends on the main clause for its meaning.	**Writing AF5** Vary sentences for clarity, purpose and effect **Writing AF6** Write with technical accuracy of syntax and punctuation in phrases, clauses and sentences	116
Join-up jigsaw		**Join-up jigsaw** is about connectives, although this term is not yet introduced to the children. These words help the children to compose compound and complex sentences, some of which include subordination involving time and reason. Ask them to read the two sections of each sentence and ask if they could be sentences in their own right, and how we can tell. Scan pictures of objects and scenes and display them on an interactive whiteboard, with text boxes in which the children can write adjectives. Ask them to write two adjectives to describe each item or scene. Save all their pairs of adjectives for comparison during the plenary session.		117

			118	**Writing AF5** Vary sentences for clarity, purpose and effect **Writing AF6** Write with technical accuracy of syntax and punctuation in phrases, clauses and sentences
Smart verbs	**11. Sentence structure and punctuation** Compose sentences using adjectives, verbs and nouns for precision, clarity and impact	**Smart verbs** develops the children's learning about verbs by asking them to choose appropriate verbs to fill gaps in sentences. It focuses on verbs with similar meanings but which can create different effects. Ask the children if the completed captions are sentences, and how they can tell. Draw out that they make sense and tell the reader something.		

Year 3 Non-fiction: Unit 1 Reports

Activity name	Strand and learning objectives	Notes on the activities	Page number	Assessment Focus
Portrait patter Signs Egg challenge: 1 and 2	**1. Speaking** Explain process or present information, ensuring items are clearly sequenced, relevant details are included and accounts ended effectively	**Portrait patter** provides a format that will help the children to present information about a portrait. You could use it in connection with work in art and design after talking to the children about other portraits and helping them to describe the details they notice and to become aware of any symbols in the portrait and why the sitter might have chosen to be pictured wearing those clothes and with those objects (or why the artist might have chosen to paint the person in this way). Useful portraits (paintings or photographs) include: *Mona Lisa or Portrait of an Old Woman* (Leonardo da Vinci), *The Graham Children* (William Hogarth), *Portrait with a Bandaged Ear* (Vincent Van Gogh), *The Daughters of Edward D. Boit* (John Singer Sargent), *The Bellelli Family* (Edgar Degas), *Napoleon in his Study* (Jacques-Louis David), *The Family of Charles IV* (Francisco Goya), *Thomas Lister* (Sir Joshua Reynolds), *Zandra Rhodes* (Norman Parkinson), *Queen Elizabeth II & Corgi* (Michael Leonard). **Vocabulary:** *artist, information, objects, portrait, sitter, sketch, symbol.* **Signs** provides a context that will help the children give a description that includes relevant details or to present information about what a sign means to them. After they have described the signs for the others to draw, you could ask them whether they have seen the sign before and, if so, where. They could first talk about it with a partner and share what they know, before telling a larger group. During the plenary session discuss how well the signs were described and which ones the children managed to draw the most accurately from the description. They could say what they thought was good about the way any of the others talked. Discuss what they have learned from one another about signs. They could also bring in pictures of signs they have seen and tell the class where they saw them, what they mean and how they are used. This page can be used in conjunction with work in RE on signs and symbols. **Vocabulary:** *sign, symbol.* **Egg challenge: 1 and 2.** In this activity the children use and develop literacy skills (scanning and skimming texts and making notes) as they carry out research tasks. During one lesson the children could discuss the challenge and who will do each piece of research, and carry out their research. They could then present reports to their groups during another lesson. Encourage volunteers to present their reports to the class during the plenary session. you could also discuss how the containers could be put to the test and how to choose which ones to post. Point out that the consideration of cost needs to be balanced against the effectiveness of the container. **Vocabulary:** *ask, design, eye contact, listen, main points, notes, present, presentation, question, report, research, share, speak, task.*	119 120 121–122	**Speaking and listening AF1** Talk in purposeful and imaginative ways to explore ideas and feelings, adapting and varying structure and vocabulary according to purpose, listeners, and content
History on screen	**2. Listening and responding** Identify the presentational features used to communicate the main points in a broadcast	**History on screen** develops skills in recognising presentational features used to give information in a broadcast. It is useful first to have watched broadcasts with the children and drawn their attention to the ways in which information is given: for example, a presenter talking, a voice-over with a picture (photograph, painting or drawing from the time or made afterwards), artefact, map, chart or action scene, text on screen, re-enactment. The children could also plan their own 'history programme' about what they have found out in connection with a history topic such as the Romans, Anglo-Saxons or the Vikings, children in the Second World War, their local area in the past or rich and poor children in Tudor times. Their broadcast could include some of the presentation methods they have identified, with different groups working on a different aspect of the topic and using different presentational methods. The children should think about and comment on what makes each presentational approach suitable for each kind of information/purpose. **Vocabulary:** *artefact, broadcast, chart, communicate, information, presentation, presenter, re-enactment, voice-over.*	123	**Speaking and listening AF4** Understand the range and uses of spoken language, commenting on meaning and impact and draw on this when talking to others
Spot the scene change: 1 and 2	**2. Listening and responding** Identify key sections of an informative broadcast, noting how the language used signals, changes or transitions in focus	**Spot the scene change: 1** and **2** support the children in identifying key sections of a broadcast, noting how language and other presentational features signal changes or transition in focus. Page 125 provides an example of how page 126 might be completed. The topic here is from RE, but you could use these pages to support work in any subject. **Vocabulary:** *feature, presentation, scene, scene change.*	124–125	**Speaking and listening AF4** Understand the range and uses of spoken language, commenting on meaning and impact and draw on this when talking to others
Make a note A non-chronological report	**7. Understanding and interpreting texts** Identify and make notes on the main points of section(s) of text	**Make a note** develops skills in using a chart for making notes. The children could highlight or underline the key words and phrases in the passage which give the information they are asked to record. **A non-chronological report** develops skills in making and reading notes. The emphasis here is on identifying key points and making notes about them briefly and in a way which can be understood later.	126 127	**Reading AF2** Understand, describe, select or retrieve information, events or ideas from texts and use quotation and reference to text **Reading AF3** Deduce, infer or interpret information, events or ideas from texts **Reading AF1** Use a range of strategies including accurate decoding of text, to read for meaning **Reading AF4** Identify and comment on the structure and organisation of texts, including grammatical and presentational features at text level **Reading AF5** Explain and comment on writers' uses of language, including grammatical and literary features at word and sentence level

Activity name	Strand and learning objectives	Notes on the activities	Assessment Focus	Page number
Sentences from notes	**9. Creating and shaping texts** Write non-narrative texts using structures of different text types	**Sentences from notes** promotes skills in developing notes into sentences and in punctuating sentences. The children also have an opportunity to group the sentences into paragraphs on a related topic. Point out that a report gives information; it does not tell a story.	All Writing AFs, especially: **Writing AF1** Write imaginative, interesting and thoughtful texts	128
Report from sentences		**Report from sentences** helps the children to structure a report with sentences grouped in paragraphs according to topic. They also develop skills in sentence structure. You could ask them what each paragraph is about. What heading would they give each paragraph?	**Writing AF2** Produce texts which are appropriate to task, reader and purpose	129
Monster report		**Monster report** is about planning the contents of a report and using the structure provided to help to organise notes, which can later be written as sentences. Emphasise the difference between this and a story about a monster: it does not tell a story but gives information. Also draw attention to the present-tense verbs and compare them with narrative sentences from a story or other recount.	**Writing AF7** Select appropriate and effective vocabulary	130
Three sets	**10. Text structure and organisation** Group related material into paragraphs	**Three sets** is about grouping related topics into paragraphs. If necessary you could help the children to group the sentences by reading the first sentence aloud and showing the children how to find another on the same topic through 'thinking aloud': for example, 'Most wood is strong, so it is good for building. That's about what wood is used for, and why. ...Here's another about what wood is used for: 'Some large everyday things we use that can be made of wood are chairs, tables, shelves, beds and cupboards.' 'Can you find another sentence about what wood is used for?' Similarly, you could start with a sentence about hard/soft wood. Once the children have grouped the sentences you could remind them of the term paragraph for a group of sentences. Remind them of their use of paragraphs in stories and explain that a report is not a story, so each paragraph is about the same topic. After they have grouped the sentences the children could decide in which order they could be written and in which order the groups should be placed in a report. Demonstrate how to introduce a report.	**Writing AF3** Organise and present whole texts effectively, sequencing and structuring information, ideas and events **Writing AF4** Construct paragraphs and use cohesion within and between paragraphs	131
Paragraph boxes		**Paragraph boxes** helps the children to group sentences in paragraphs according to topic in order to structure a report. They also develop skills in converting notes into sentences. This could be linked with work in geography on the local environment.		132
Report plan		**Report plan** provides an opportunity for the children to use what they have learned about grouping related material into paragraphs: they write their own simple report about sheep, based on annotated pictures provided. Ask them what they can find out from each picture and notes. They should form a sentence about this and decide in which paragraph to write it.		133
Report improver		**Report improver** develops skills in editing and provides an opportunity for the children to use success criteria and to use them to evaluate writing. Read the first sentence aloud and ask the children if it is a good sentence. Underline each and and ask them what they notice. How can they improve the sentence? Would it be better split into two or more sentences? Discuss how: for example, *There are magic spells in a lot of stories. Cinderella is one of them. In this story a fairy turns a pumpkin into a coach, mice into horses, lizards into footmen and old rags into a lovely ball gown.* It is particularly valuable to allow pairs to discuss the editing options aloud in this activity; Reviewing the text with a partner allows them to hear and internalise sentence structures.		134
Go with the flow	**11. Sentence structure and punctuation** Show relationships of time, reason and cause, through subordination and connectives	**Go with the flow** reinforces the children's learning about connective words in compound sentences involving time. It is useful to draw out that these words help to communicate information about the order in which events happen, especially in a fiction or non-fiction recount.	**Writing AF5** Vary sentences for clarity, purpose and effect **Writing AF6** Write with technical accuracy of syntax and punctuation in phrases, clauses and sentences	135
Reporting sentences	**11. Sentence structure and punctuation** Compose sentences using adjectives, verbs and nouns for precision, clarity and impact	**Reporting sentences** helps the children to recognise the style of a non-chronological report. Draw out how these sentences are different from the sentences used in instructions or recounts by focusing on the person and on the form and tense of the verb.	**Writing AF5** Vary sentences for clarity, purpose and effect **Writing AF6** Write with technical accuracy of syntax and punctuation in phrases, clauses and sentences	136

Year 3 Non-fiction: Unit 2 Instructions

Activity name	Strand and learning objectives	Notes on the activities	Assessment Focus	Page number
Picture this: 1 and 2	**1. Speaking** Explain process or present information, ensuring items are clearly sequenced, relevant details are included and accounts ended effectively	**Picture this: 1** and **2** provide a context and structure for presenting information that includes relevant detail. Remind the children of their previous learning about speaking clearly, looking at their audience and using expression. Here they could try to make the picture sound interesting, perhaps by beginning with something that is happening in it: for example, rather than saying 'There are a lot of people on the beach' they could say 'The beach was packed with children playing and adults sunbathing and a queue was growing at the ice cream stall.' They could make a note of useful and interesting words to use in their descriptions: many of these will be adjectives and verbs. First let the children listen to passages from a radio broadcast in which a scene is described. Ask them to imagine the scene and to say whether they have enough information to do so and, if not, what else they need to know. They could then present this as a radio broadcast, speaking from behind a screen. **Vocabulary:** *describe, detail, different, observant, observe.*	**Speaking and listening AF1** Talk in purposeful and imaginative ways to explore ideas and feelings, adapting and varying structure and vocabulary according to purpose, listeners, and content	137–138

Activity	Page	Objective (AF)	Strand and objective	Teacher notes
Jumble sale	139	**Speaking and listening AF2** Listen and respond to others, including in pairs and groups, shaping meanings through suggestions, comments, and questions	**3. Group discussion and interaction** Use discussion to organise roles and action	**Jumble sale.** This provides opportunities to include work in citizenship and mathematics. Discuss the children's experiences of jumble sales and identify the tasks which had to be carried out before, during and after the event: choosing a time, date and place, and notifying people so that they can donate goods and attend the event; organising furniture and containers for money; deciding what should be sold and on how many different stalls; allocating helpers to the stalls, thanking them and letting them know how much money was raised and how it was spent. For the extension activity, you could help the children to plan using a diary or calendar in order to identify deadlines for each task. **Vocabulary:** allocate, choose, identify, list, organise, rota, task.
Our school grounds	140	**Speaking and listening AF2** Listen and respond to others, including in pairs and groups, shaping meanings through suggestions, comments, and questions	**3. Group discussion and interaction** Actively include and respond to all members of the group	**Our school grounds** focuses on actively including and involving all members of the group. The term 'buzz points' is a useful term for referring to talking points that everyone shows interest in and contributes to. Each child in the group should express a view on the statements about the school grounds and justify it. Those who agree should say why and any who disagree should also offer a reason, expressed politely and sensitively, using words such as because, but, so, what about. You could take them out to look at the school grounds so that they can check any assumptions they make. The activity links well with work in geography on the school grounds. **Vocabulary:** agree, because, buzz point, consider, disagree, discuss, listen.
I disagree	141			**I disagree** is about responding to other members of the group. The children consider and discuss how to change the impolite comments so that others might accept these views because they are expressed politely. Ask them to express each of the comments below in the following two ways – one that will encourage the other person to agree or to accept it and one in a way that would make them want to disagree or reject it: No, I don't want to do that, I do not like that, I think that is wrong. Remind them to add a reason or explanation to their comment. **Vocabulary:** agree, because, disagree, impolite, rude, so, that.
Base words with the suffix -tion	142	**Writing AF8** Use correct spelling	**6. Word structure and spelling** Recognise a range of prefixes and suffixes, understanding how they modify meaning and spelling, and how they assist in decoding long, complex words	**Base words with the suffix -tion** helps the children to understand how nouns are formed by adding the suffix **-tion** to base words. Explain how the **-tion** suffix transforms verbs into nouns. Use the words in sentences to show how their meanings change: for example, I can inform you about the buses/I can give you information about the buses. (Also demonstrate incorrect sentences: I confess what I did was wrong/I made a confession about what I did wrong.) The children learn how the suffix affects the spelling and meaning of the base word: for example, base words ending in **-ct** or **-nt** lose the **t**, words ending in **-ate** lose the **te**, words ending in **-y** lose the **y** and add **ica**. They could compare words in the list with others, such as adopt/adoption, amplify/amplification, apply/application, collect/collection, construct/construction, corrupt/corruption, digest/digestion, detect/detection, falsify/falsification, insulate/insulation, isolate/isolation, justify/justification, locate/location, nominate/nomination, protect/protection, purify/purification, rotate/rotation, select/selection, translate/translation. Ask them to notice any that do not fit the pattern. After completing the activity they could group the base words according to how they changed, and notice any patterns.
Making sense with -sion	143			**Making sense with -sion** helps the children to understand how nouns are formed by adding the suffix **-sion** to base words. Explain how the **-sion** suffix transforms verbs into nouns. Use the words in sentences to show how their meanings change: for example, I confess what I did was wrong/I made a confession about what I did wrong. The children learn how the suffix affects the spelling and meaning of the base word: for example, base words ending in **-ss** lose the final **s**, words ending in **-de** following a vowel lose the **de** and add **s**, words ending in **-se** following a vowel lose the **se**. They could compare the words in the list with others, such as provide/provision, supervise/supervision (although many **-ise** words lose the **s** and add **-ation**: for example, improvisation). Ask them to notice any that do not fit the pattern. After completing the activity they could group the base words according to how they changed, and notice any patterns.
It's like this	144			**It's like this** is concerned with recognising suffixes and understanding how they modify meaning and spelling. It focuses on the suffix **-like** for forming adjectives from nouns. It is important to point out that the base word is always unchanged and to compare this with the addition of other suffixes. Point out that the suffix **-like** begins with a consonant and ask the children to check whether other suffixes beginning with a consonant change the base word. (some do: for example, merry/merriment, happy/happily.
Words with usefulness	145			**Words with usefulness** is concerned with recognising suffixes and understanding how they modify meaning and spelling. It focuses on the suffix **-ness** for forming nouns from adjectives. Other useful words include boldness, brightness, coolness, faithfulness, feebleness, fussiness, heaviness, holiness, keenness, laziness, lightness, meanness, nearness, paleness, prettiness, quickness, quietness, richness, ripeness, roughness, selfishness, sleepiness, slenderness, softness, smoothness, straightness, sweetness, thankfulness, wetness, wickedness. Ask the children to notice the type of word to which **-ness** is added. Ask them if the base word changes before the suffix is added and, if so, whether they can spot any patterns. Note that **y** following a consonant (or double consonant or two different consonants) changes to **i** apart from a few exceptions, such as sly/slyness (happy/happiness, salty/saltiness, silly/silliness); if the base words ends with **n**, the **n** of **-ness** makes this a double **n** (meanness, sternness). You could challenge the children to look for exceptions to the rules.
Opposites with il-, im- or in-	146			**Opposites with il-, im- or in-** is concerned with recognising prefixes and understanding how they modify meaning and spelling. It focuses on the use of prefixes that create adjectives with opposite meanings to the base adjectives. Useful rules to draw out: words beginning with **l** usually take the prefix **il-**; words beginning **m, b** or **p** usually take the prefix **im-**; others take **in-**. These prefixes do not alter the spelling of the base word: they often produce a double consonant since the initial consonant is not dropped: illogical, immoderate, innumerate.
All wrong	147			**All wrong** is about recognising prefixes and understanding how they modify meaning and spelling. It focuses on the use of prefixes that create negative verbs and adjectives. The prefix **mis-** does not alter the spelling of the base word; it might produce a double **s** since the initial **s** is not dropped: misshapen, misspell, misspent. During the plenary session you could invite feedback about how the meanings of the words changed and if the spelling of any base word changed.
Prefix pre-	148			**Prefix pre-** focuses on recognising prefixes and understanding how they modify meaning and spelling. The sentences should help the children to figure out the meaning of **pre-**. Ask them to identify the base words from which the **pre-** words were formed and to say which ones are real words and which are not. Note that those that do not appear to be real words come from other languages, particularly Latin; for example, predict, prepare. See also page 150 for other commonly-occurring syllables.

Activity name	Strand and learning objectives	Notes on the activities	Assessment Focus	Page number
Xword	**6. Word structure and spelling** Recognise a range of prefixes and suffixes, understanding how they modify meaning and spelling, and how they assist in decoding long, complex words	**Xword** develops the children's recognition of prefixes and understanding of how they modify meaning and spelling. First explain crossword conventions: one letter (not one phoneme) per square, interlocking answers on the grid, consecutive numbering of answers (for example, why there is no number 1 across?), bracketed numbers showing the number of letters in the answers. The clues should help the children to figure out the meaning of **ex-**. Ask them to identify the base words from which the **ex-** words were formed and to say which ones are real words and which are not. Note that these do not appear to be real words. They come from other languages, particularly Latin. See also page 149 for other commonly occurring syllables.	**Writing AF8** Use correct spelling	149
Watch and note	**7. Understanding and interpreting texts** Identify and make notes on the main points of section(s) of text	**Watch and note** provides a model for making notes about a television programme about making or doing something. The children develop an appreciation of the purpose of notes and the need to write quickly and in a way that can be understood later. They could also make their own notes about a television programme that shows how to make or do something. There are opportunities for speaking and listening if they share the task in pairs.	**Reading AF2** Understand, describe, select or retrieve information, events or ideas from texts and use quotation and reference to text **Reading AF3** Deduce, infer or interpret information, events or ideas from texts **Reading AF1** Use a range of strategies including accurate decoding of text, to read for meaning **Reading AF4** Identify and comment on the structure and organisation of texts, including grammatical and presentational features at text level **Reading AF5** Explain and comment on writers' uses of language, including grammatical and literary features at word and sentence level	150
Make it	**7. Understanding and interpreting texts** Identify how different texts are organised, including reference texts, magazines, leaflets, on paper and on screen	**Make it** provides a set of instructions in random order. The children develop an appreciation for the need to present instructions in a logical order, beginning with a heading stating what the instructions are for, followed by a list of equipment and materials. Children should list the equipment needed and they might suggest illustrations too.	**Reading AF2** Understand, describe, select or retrieve information, events or ideas from texts and use quotation and reference to text **Reading AF3** Deduce, infer or interpret information, events or ideas from texts **Reading AF1** Use a range of strategies including accurate decoding of text, to read for meaning **Reading AF4** Identify and comment on the structure and organisation of texts, including grammatical and presentational features at text level **Reading AF5** Explain and comment on writers' uses of language, including grammatical and literary features at word and sentence level	151
Recount to instruction: 1 and 2		**Recount to instruction: 1** and **2** present a recount of a process and a format to help the children to convert the recount into instructions. It is important to point out the different sentence structures of the two text types and other features, such as person and tense. It could be linked with work in art or design and technology: the children could write a recount about making something and then convert their recount to instructions for someone else to follow. They could then evaluate one another's instructions. As an extension activity, ask the children to say what they changed and to explain why.		152–153
The instructions judge		**The instructions judge** encourages the children to express an opinion of a set of instructions and to support this with evidence. Some examples of instructions teachers could use include: instructions for a game, how to make something, how to set up or use equipment (such as taking photos with a digital camera, sending a text message, setting the date, time or alarm clock on a mobile phone, emailing attachments, a recipe).		154
Step by step	**10. Text structure and organisation** Signal sequence, place and time to give coherence	**Step by step** encourages the children to signal sequence to give coherence to instructions. After writing the instructions in note form they could write them in the form of sentences – perhaps keying them in and using format and layout to clarify them and make them appealing to the reader. You could ask them to try following these instructions and then, after saving them, dragging and dropping them into a different order to find out what difference it makes.	**Writing AF3** Organise and present whole texts effectively, sequencing and structuring information, ideas and events	155
Snap!		**Snap!** helps the children to write a non-narrative text (instructions) that signals the correct sequence. They might need to start and stop a game of Snap! several times to check what they need to write. You could model how to write instruction sentences with the help of volunteers, beginning by demonstrating how an instruction sentence begins (with an imperative verb, although this term will probably not be introduced yet).	**Writing AF4** Construct paragraphs and use cohesion within and between paragraphs	156
The witches' spell		**The witches' spell** helps the children to write a non-narrative text (instructions) that signals the correct sequence. It also helps to consolidate their skills in writing imperative sentences by asking them to convert a recount into instructions. You could draw attention to the words that should be changed: personal pronouns and verbs. Model how and why the sentences change: for example, *Here the witch is telling readers what they said. We need to change it to 'Abracadabra – what to do, so instead of 'We said.' I'll write 'Say'. I'll leave the rest of the sentence as it is: Say together 'Abracadabra – all teachers be cats'. That sounds like an instruction.*		157
Do this	**11. Sentence structure and punctuation** Compose sentences using adjectives, verbs and nouns for precision, clarity and impact	**Do this** and **Command verbs** focus on the verbs used in instructions. They develop the children's awareness of the style of sentence used in instructions. The children could discuss the sentences with a partner and then collaborate on the answers they write. During the plenary session it is useful to focus on the verbs used. Draw out that they are in the command form – they tell the reader what to do. These activities can be linked with text-level work on writing instructions.	**Writing AF5** Vary sentences for clarity, purpose and effect **Writing AF6** Write with technical accuracy of syntax and punctuation in phrases, clauses and sentences	158–159
Command verbs				
That's the way		**That's the way** reinforces the children's learning about the verbs used in instructions and develops their understanding of how to write instruction sentences. This activity can support work in geography on following maps to find the way to places and using a map to help in giving directions. It can also be linked with work in design and technology in which they write a report about what they have made and then convert it into instructions or a recipe which someone else could follow. The children could type up their recount of a process. Select recounts to display on an interactive whiteboard and invite volunteers to take turns to change sentences into instruction (command) form. Similarly, they could convert recipes into recounts.		160

Year 3 Non-fiction: Unit 3 Information texts

Activity name	Strand and learning objectives	Notes on the activities	Assessment Focus	Page number
Ancient Egyptians: 1 and 2	**1. Speaking** Explain process or present information, ensuring items are clearly sequenced, relevant details are included and accounts ended effectively	**Ancient Egyptians: 1 and 2** provide a context for presenting information. You could make a similar set of information cards for any other topic the children are working on so that different children can talk about a different aspect of the subject in order to share their learning with the class. It is useful to make this process explicit: tell the children that they are going to help one another to learn about the Ancient Egyptians by sharing what they have learned. In addition to preparing a short talk about the information on the card, the children could use information texts or other sources to find out more about the aspect of the topic on their card. An important part of the process will be reflecting on the task afterwards: how well the children presented their information, what they found difficult and so on. As reading the information on the cards is an important part of this activity, provide any help that is necessary for reading unfamiliar words and phrases. Useful sources include *Arts and Crafts of Ancient Egypt* by Ting Morris (Franklin Watts), *All About Ancient Peoples: the Egyptians* by Anita Ganeri (Franklin Watts), *Eyewitness: Ancient Egypt* by Jen Green (Dorling Kindersley), *Encyclopedia of Ancient Egypt* (Usborne), *The Egyptian Echo* by Paul Dowswell (Usborne), *Who was Cleopatra?* by Geraldine Harris (Macdonald), *History Detectives: Ancient Egypt* by Philip Ardagh (Macmillan). **Vocabulary:** *information, learn, present, share, talk.*	**Speaking and listening AF1** Talk in purposeful and imaginative ways to explore ideas and feelings, adapting and varying structure and vocabulary according to purpose, listeners, and content	161–162
The root of the matter	**3. Group discussion and interaction** Use discussion to organise roles and action	**The root of the matter.** Before writing notes the children should wait for each speaker to finish, or one child could act as scribe. They should write only the main points. The children should listen to the ideas of each member of their group before discussing the merits of each one and deciding which will best help them to answer the question. They can then decide who will do what. Help them to rotate tasks such as writing, fetching equipment and tidying up during the course of a week. **Vocabulary:** *answer, ask, discuss, listen, notes, question, take turns.*	**Speaking and listening AF2** Listen and respond to others, including in pairs and groups, shaping meanings through suggestions, comments, and questions	163
A good discussion	**3. Group discussion and interaction** Actively include and respond to all members of the group	**A good discussion.** Ask the children how the behaviour of the others in the group might affect how Ellie feels about making a presentation to them. Discuss which of them encourage her and how: for example, using her name and asking questions. The extension activity links with text-level work on writing letters. **Vocabulary:** *ask, discussion, eye contact, listen, present, presentation, question, report, speak.*	**Speaking and listening AF2** Listen and respond to others, including in pairs and groups, shaping meanings through suggestions, comments, and questions	164
Persuaders	**8. Engaging with and responding to texts** Identify features that writers use to provoke readers reactions	**Persuaders** introduces simple persuasive texts to develop the children's understanding of how a text is presented in order to persuade people to do or buy something. Use the annotate tool on the interactive whiteboard to record children's observations and comments. As a further extension children could look for other examples in magazines, local newspapers, leaflets, etc.	All Reading AFs, especially: **Reading AF6** Identify and comment on writers' purposes and viewpoints and the overall effect of the text on the reader **Reading AF3** Deduce, infer or interpret information, events or ideas from texts **Reading AF7** Relate texts to their social, cultural and historical contexts and literary traditions	165
No-cook chocolate slice: 1 and 2	**9. Creating and shaping texts** Write non-narrative texts using structures of different text types	**No-cook chocolate slice: 1 and 2** show the children how to write a non-narrative text using the format of a recipe. Page 167 presents a picture recipe from which the children find out how to make no-cook chocolate slice. They give instructions orally to a partner. Invite feedback and notice whether the children are using the imperative (command) form of the verbs. If they begin each sentence with You, demonstrate how to change their sentence into an instruction, with reference to a sentence from a recipe book. Point out that the word You is not needed. To test the instructions they could take turns to tell a partner what to do while their partner actually carries out the instructions, after which they could write their recipe in the form of sentences.	All Writing AFs, especially: **Writing AF1** Write imaginative, interesting and thoughtful texts **Writing AF2** Produce texts which are appropriate to task, reader and purpose **Writing AF7** Select appropriate and effective vocabulary	166–167
Fact-finder		**Fact-finder** provides an opportunity for the children to note information collected from reading more than one source in order to write an information text about teeth. This has links with their work in science. They should use both written and on-screen resources. Model how to find information through using the contents page, index, chapter headings and picture captions and, on websites, the site map, links and tabs.		168
Now wash your hands		**Now wash your hands** helps the children to write an information poster for younger children so that they use information to persuade them to wash their hands. They could use the same information to help them to plan and present an audio or video presentation.		169
School dinners School dinners cards	**9. Creating and shaping texts** Select and use a range of technical and descriptive vocabulary	**School dinners** and **School dinners cards** help the children to begin to use words in an information text to persuade others, selecting and using technical vocabulary and using layout and formatting graphics and illustrations in order to produce a persuasive report. They could carry out their research during science lessons on healthy eating. Remind them of the need to record where they found the facts in case they need to be checked or so that more information can be found out.	All Writing AFs, especially: **Writing AF1** Write imaginative, interesting and thoughtful texts **Writing AF2** Produce texts which are appropriate to task, reader and purpose **Writing AF7** Select appropriate and effective vocabulary	170–171

Year 3 Poetry: Unit 1 Poems to perform

Activity name	Strand and learning objectives	Notes on the activities	Assessment Focus	Page number
Bedtime Wonderful worms	**9. Creating and shaping texts** Use layout, format, graphics, illustrations for different purposes	**Bedtime and Wonderful worms** help the children to explore a persuasive scenario through role-play, having collected information from different sources. They learn how to use and present information in order to persuade. This prepares for later work on persuasive texts and arguments and can be linked with work in citizenship on making choices. To find facts about recycling in general and wormeries in particular, see websites such as: http://www.recyclezone.org.uk/ http://www.recyclingconsortium.org.uk/schools/ http://www.activityvillage.co.uk/recycling_for_kids.htm http://www.recycle-more.co.uk/nav/page560.aspx http://www.wormcity.co.uk/wormfaq.htm http://www.originalorganics.co.uk/wormeries.htm http://www.thekidsgarden.co.uk/MakingAWormery.html	All Writing AFs, especially: **Writing AF1** Write imaginative, interesting and thoughtful texts **Writing AF2** Produce texts which are appropriate to task, reader and purpose **Writing AF7** Select appropriate and effective vocabulary	172–173
Time sentences Place to place	**11. Sentence structure and punctuation** Compose sentences using adjectives, verbs and nouns for precision, clarity and impact	**Time sentences** focuses on the use of adverbial phrases of time, although this term is not yet introduced. It develops the children's understanding of the purposes of words and groups of words in sentences. The children could begin by reading each example and saying whether or not it is a sentence. Draw out that they are all sentences and that the children are going to add extra information about when the action took place. **Place to place** focuses on the use of adverbial phrases of place, although this term is not yet introduced. It develops the children's understanding of the purposes of words and groups of words in sentences. The children could begin by reading each example and saying whether or not it is a sentence. Draw out that they are all sentences and that the children are going to add extra information – about where the action took place.	**Writing AF5** Vary sentences for clarity, purpose and effect **Writing AF6** Write with technical accuracy of syntax and punctuation in phrases, clauses and sentences	174 175

Year 3 Poetry: Unit 1 Poems to perform

Activity name	Strand and learning objectives	Notes on the activities	Assessment Focus	Page number
Dark The train De bottleman	**1. Speaking** Choose and prepare poems or stories for performance, identifying appropriate expression, tone, volume and use of voices and other sounds	**Dark** provides a poem for performance. It helps the children to understand what is meant by 'expression' and to focus on aspects of using their voices for expression: volume, tone, speed and pace. You could read the poem aloud while they follow it on their copy of the page before they read it to themselves, and then read it aloud individually. They can then discuss it with a partner or group – pairings/groupings should give opportunities for less confident readers to hear/learn the poem and contribute ideas for interpretation. Ask the children to identify the ways in which their voices should change as they read. Ask them how the font size helps at the end. You could link this activity with work on creating and shaping texts (writing poems modelled on another). For the final performance, the children could record their reading. **Vocabulary:** *atmosphere, expression, fast, feeling, font, loud, pace, pause, quiet, recite, slow, speed, tone, volume.* **The Train** provides a poem for performance. It helps the children to understand what is meant by 'expression' and to focus on aspects of using their voices for expression, focusing mainly on volume and rhythm. They could say *jickety-can, jickettycan* over and over again and notice the natural rhythm of these invented words. Ask them to read the short lines of the second verse with the same rhythm. They should find that they do this naturally because of the line lengths and the onomatopoeic sounds of the words used. **Vocabulary:** *atmosphere, expression, fade, fast, loud, onomatopoeia, quiet, recite, repeat, repetition, rhythm, slow, volume.* **De Bottleman.** Ask the children if they know what a 'bottleman' is. They can find out from the poem. Children from the Caribbean might be familiar with the sound and sight of a bottleman (or have heard about them from members of their families). **Vocabulary:** *call, dialect, recite, sound, voice.*	**Speaking and listening AF1** Talk in purposeful and imaginative ways to explore ideas and feelings, adapting and varying structure and vocabulary according to purpose, listeners, and content	176 177 178
This is the greatest!	**3. Group discussion and interaction** Actively include and respond to all members of the group	**This is the greatest!** After each speaker has presented their argument, the others may challenge what has been said: for example, one speaker might argue that without light bulbs people would not be able to see at night; another may respond that fire is more important because it not only provides light, but also gives out heat for warmth and for cooking. Draw out that a challenge is neither a confrontation nor an attack, but shows that the other person has been listening; a challenge can also help the speaker to express ideas more clearly. **Vocabulary:** *ask, challenge, eye contact, listen, notes, present, presentation, question, speak, vote.*	**Speaking and listening AF2** Listen and respond to others, including in pairs and groups, shaping meanings through suggestions, comments, and questions	179
Actions speak louder Face to face	**4. Drama** Identify and discuss qualities of others' performances, including gesture, action and costume	**Actions speak louder.** While watching a video you could stop at different points and ask the children to mime the gestures and actions of one of the characters. Discuss what the character was doing and the emotions involved. **Vocabulary:** *action, character, emotion, gesture, mime, portray, scene.* **Face to face** could be linked with work in art on portraits. The children could label copies of works of art according to what they think the person feels. To support work in history, they could make Greek theatre masks to be worn during performances of Greek myths. **Vocabulary:** *action, character, drama, emotion, facial, expression, feeling, mask, theatre.*	**Speaking and listening AF4** Understand the range and uses of spoken language, commenting on meaning and impact and draw on this when talking to others	180 181
Sounds the same Compound word dominoes: 1 and 2	**6. Word structure and spelling** Spell high and medium frequency words	**Sounds the same** develops the children's ability to spell high-frequency homophones through understanding, where appropriate, the morphological rules of their context. In addition to *road/rode*, you could add *rowed* and ask the children to read the word and suggest a sentence for it. Point out the **-ed** ending and ask them what this tells them about the word. **Compound word dominoes: 1** and **2** help the children to learn the spellings of medium- and high-frequency words. They should be able to use phonics to read the individual words from which compound words can be made. Use the CD-ROM to edit these pages, to provide extra words and perhaps repeats of some of the existing words, but in different combinations.	**Writing AF8** Use correct spelling	182 183–184

Activity name	Strand and learning objectives	Notes on the activities	Assessment Focus	Page number
All in a day's work	**7. Understanding and interpreting texts** Explore how different texts appeal to readers using varied sentence structures and descriptive language	**All in a day's work** introduces poems or songs created by people in different types of work. These can be linked with work in citizenship on living in a diverse world. Focus on the rhythm of each song and how it reflects the work it is connected with. Talk about the work featured in each poem and mime it before inviting the children to join in and then to recite or sing the song. Focus on the way in which the rhythm of the song matches the rhythm of the movements of the workers. *Hoe Emma Hoe* was sung by cotton and sugar plantation workers (slaves) in the USA and Jamaica. Slave work gangs used call-and-response work songs like this to regulate the pace of their work. The songs were also used to talk about their masters, overseers and their work conditions. The slaves had to be careful about expressing opinions so they often sang in 'code', which they, but not their masters, would understand. *Casey Jones* is about an engine driver in the USA. John Luther 'Casey' Jones was from Jackson, Tennessee. He lived from 1863–1900 and worked for the Illinois Central Railroad (IC). In 1900 he was the only fatality on a foggy, wet night when his train collided with a stationary freight train at Vaughan, Mississippi. This song immortalised him as a hero after trying to stop his train to save lives. *The Volga Boatmen's Song* is a shanty song by bargemen in Russia. *Leave Her Johnny, Leave Her* was a sea shanty sung by sailors hauling on ropes to moor ships. *Dark as the Dungeon* was sung by miners in the USA. Teachers could use something like *Row, row, row your boat* (although this was not a work song) to get children thinking about the way songs and actions/movements can complement one another.	**Reading AF2** Understand, describe, select or retrieve information, events or ideas from texts and use quotation and reference to text **Reading AF3** Deduce, infer or interpret information, events or ideas from texts **Reading AF1** Use a range of strategies including accurate decoding of text, to read for meaning **Reading AF4** Identify and comment on the structure and organisation of texts, including grammatical and presentational features at text level **Reading AF5** Explain and comment on writers' uses of language, including grammatical and literary features at word and sentence level	185
Elimination poem	**8. Engaging with and responding to texts** Identify features that writers use to provoke readers reactions	**Elimination poem** focuses on the distinctive pattern of a poem with a repetitive structure that includes dialogue. There is also an opportunity to identify features writers use to provoke readers' reactions. It is useful to remind the children of similar, much simpler rhymes they will have learned in the past, such as *Ten Green Bottles*. Encourage them to plan how to read and perform it in a way that reflects the diminishing number of trees. The entire class could read the first verse, with some dropping out each time a tree is felled. The spoken words in the third line of each verse could be read by an individual. You could also ask the children what the poet wants readers to consider about the felling of trees and how they can tell. Which words reveal the poet's feelings? Discuss who wants to fell the trees, and why, and point out words such as *boomed, screamed, snarled* and *grumped*. Discuss the ending of the poem and the impression it creates of emptiness with words such as 'in vain', 'empty skylines' and 'cold, grey rain'. Compare this with the scene where there were trees, at the beginning of the poem: 'Ten tall oaktrees, Standing in a line' and 'Nine tall oaktrees, Growing tall and straight', 'Eight tall oaktrees, Reaching towards heaven'.	All Reading AFs, especially: **Reading AF6** Identify and comment on writers' purposes and viewpoints and the overall effect of the text on the reader **Reading AF3** Deduce, infer or interpret information, events or ideas from texts **Reading AF7** Relate texts to their social, cultural and historical contexts and literary traditions	186

Year 3 Poetry: Unit 2 Shape poetry and calligrams

Activity name	Strand and learning objectives	Notes on the activities	Assessment Focus	Page number
Packing to go	**1. Speaking** Sustain conversation, explain or give reasons for their views or choices	**Packing to go.** The children could first discuss in pairs what they would not want to leave behind. They could begin with a long list and then eliminate items. Ask them to tell their partner why some items are more important to them than others. **Vocabulary:** choice, choose, explain, reason, role-play.	**Speaking and listening AF2** Listen and respond to others, including in pairs and groups, shaping meanings through suggestions, comments, and questions	187
Short story Shorten it	**6. Word structure and spelling** Spell high and medium frequency words	**Short story** and **Shorten it** help the children to spell high frequency words through understanding how contractions are formed by combining two words, dropping one or more letters and inserting an apostrophe in their place. You could introduce this by writing the words in full, deleting the letters to be omitted, deleting the gap between the words and inserting an apostrophe. Children should use their own wipe-off boards to try out the contractions, as necessary. The children could also try this using the computer and interactive whiteboard: *I will, I shall; we had, you had, they have, I have, we have; they are, we are, you are; I would, you would, they would; shall not, should not, could not.* When children write their instructions for contractions, give them guidance about where/what letter is left out and replaced with an apostrophe, by asking: *Is it always a vowel? Does the position of the vowel matter?* Ask the children who tackle the extension activity to begin by listing all the contractions they know and then to think about the rules and whether all their examples meet them. They should notice that *can't, shan't* and *won't* don't follow the rules.	**Writing AF8** Use correct spelling	188–189
Fun shapes	**8. Engaging with and responding to texts** Identify features that writers use to provoke readers reactions	**Fun shapes** introduces poetic shapes that play with the meanings of words, drawing on double meanings. These are true shape poems. From this activity the children learn to identify features that writers use to provoke readers' reactions: the clever use of letters that sound like the words they begin, combined with shapes, to create 'word-pictures' such as *teapot, beehive, eye, OK, peanut, seashell, DJ, delight*. Ask them to say the names of the letters and to look at the shapes (the *t*s are shaped like a teapot, the *b*s are in the shape of a hive, the *i*s are in the shape of an eye, the *o*s are in the shape of a *k*, the *p*s are in the shape of a nut, the *c*s are in the shape of a shell, the *d*s are in the shape of a *J* and the *d*s are in the shape of a light. In the extension activity ask them to think of *b*s in the shape of 4, *c*s in the shape of a gull and *r*s in the shape of the word *me*. A shape poem is one in which the layout of the words reflects the shape or an aspect of the subject. It can include plays on words.	All Reading AFs, especially: **Reading AF6** Identify and comment on writers' purposes and viewpoints and the overall effect of the text on the reader **Reading AF3** Deduce, infer or interpret information, events or ideas from texts **Reading AF7** Relate texts to their social, cultural and historical contexts and literary traditions	190
Penguin	**9. Creating and shaping texts** Select and use a range of technical and descriptive vocabulary	**Penguin** encourages the children to select and use a range of descriptive vocabulary to communicate the way in which a penguin moves.	All Writing AFs, especially: **Writing AF1** Write imaginative, interesting and thoughtful texts **Writing AF2** Produce texts which are appropriate to task, reader and purpose **Writing AF7** Select appropriate and effective vocabulary	191

Year 3 Poetry: Unit 2 (continued)

Activity name	Strand and learning objectives	Notes on the activities	Assessment Focus	Page number
Word shapes Flat fish and wiggly worms Waterfall Sunflower	**9. Creating and shaping texts** Use layout, format, graphics, illustrations for different purposes	**Word shapes** encourages the children to draw on their knowledge and experience of calligrams to help them to write words in a way that expresses their meaning. **Flat fish and wiggly worms** encourages the children to draw on their knowledge and experience of calligrams to help them to write their own. They could first try out some phrases and sentences orally. Also make use of interactive whiteboard software that facilitates the creation of calligrams as suggested in the Primary Framework for Literacy. **Waterfall** and **Sunflower** encourage the children to use what they have learned from reading shape poems to help them to write their own, using appropriate presentational devices. They provide structures to support their writing but some children might be able to draw their own. Alternatively, they could watch a recording of a waterfall or look at a photograph of a sunflower on an interactive whiteboard and use the appropriate software to key in text onto the picture and to arrange it to mimic the shape of the subject.	All Writing AFs, especially: **Writing AF1** Write imaginative, interesting and thoughtful texts **Writing AF2** Produce texts which are appropriate to task, reader and purpose **Writing AF7** Select appropriate and effective vocabulary	192 193 194–195
A sentence in any shape	**11. Sentence structure and punctuation** Compose sentences using adjectives, verbs and nouns for precision, clarity and impact	**A sentence in any shape** helps the children to identify sentences in poems, whatever the layout. It can be linked with text-level work on writing calligrams and shape poems, which may or may not contain sentences. You could model how to write interesting sentences using the interactive whiteboard. Begin with *A snake went across the grass* and ask the children to think of a better verb than *went* to say how a snake might move: for example, *slithered, wriggled, slid*. Discuss a more interesting way to say *across the garden*. You could add adjectives and other words to give the reader an impression of the garden and a picture of the snake slithering: *between the tall blades of grass*. The final sentence might be *The snake slithered between the tall blades of grass*. Ask the children which sentence gives them a clearer picture of the scene, and how.	**Writing AF5** Vary sentences for clarity, purpose and effect **Writing AF6** Write with technical accuracy of syntax and punctuation in phrases, clauses and sentences	196

Year 3 Poetry: Unit 3 Language play

Activity name	Strand and learning objectives	Notes on the activities	Assessment Focus	Page number
You're joking! How loud?	**1. Speaking** Choose and prepare poems or stories for performance, identifying appropriate expression, tone, volume and use of voices and other sounds	**You're joking!** is about preparing material for performance: identifying appropriate expression, tone, volume and use of voices and other sounds. Jokes have been selected for the children, but they could also make their own collection of jokes and practise telling them effectively. You could model different ways of reading each line and ask the children which they think sounds the best before they try them out for themselves. It is useful to pair less confident children with others who are more confident. The less confident child could speak from behind the door (use the classroom door or a cupboard door). **Vocabulary:** *aggressively, angrily, bad-tempered, expression, gently, joke, sing-song, sound, sound effect*. **How loud?** focuses on preparing a poem for performance, with the emphasis on volume. This poem could also support work on understanding and responding to texts (patterns on the page). The children will learn how the way in which a poem is presented on the page affects the way in which we read it: here the font size and highlighting is particularly effective. The children should notice changes from lower to upper case, changes in font size, and punctuation such as exclamation marks. Ask them about the tone of the poem: happy, sad, serious, funny, exciting, calm. You could read the part of the teacher with children reading the part of Andrew. **Vocabulary:** *font, funny, loud, louder, loudest, loudness, quiet, tone, volume*.	**Speaking and listening AF1** Talk in purposeful and imaginative ways to explore ideas and feelings, adapting and varying structure and vocabulary according to purpose, listeners, and content	197 198
Tell me more	**1. Speaking** Sustain conversation, explain or give reasons for their views or choices	**Tell me more** can support work in citizenship on choices, understanding right and wrong and the work of the police. Ask what people should do if they witness a theft. What difference does it make if the thief is a friend? Invite volunteers to contribute to a list of courses of action which they think are right and which also help the friend. **Vocabulary:** *ask, choose, conversation, explain, listen, opinion, question, right, said, says, speak, views, wrong*.	**Speaking and listening AF2** Listen and respond to others, including in pairs and groups, shaping meanings through suggestions, comments, and questions	199

Activity	Objective	Description	Writing AF	Pages
Words ending -le; Words ending -el; Words ending -al; -il wordsearch	**6. Word structure and spelling** Spell high and medium frequency words	**Words ending -le. Words ending -el. Words ending -al** and **il wordsearch** develop the children's ability to read and spell high-frequency words and to learn conventions that will help them to spell other, unfamiliar, words. A useful rule is that most word endings that sound like l are spelled -le. These words can be nouns, verbs or adjectives, such as angle, brittle, cockle, little, tickle, wriggle. The children could begin databases of -le, -el, -al and -il words and notice the most common type of word with each ending. People sometimes pronounce the -il in a distinctively different way to -le and -el words. Other examples of words with the -le ending include bundle, cattle, cobble, juggle, muddle, pickle, ripple, ruffle, saddle, steeple. Words with the -el ending include angel, channel, flannel, kennel, model, panel, snorkel, travel. Words with the -al ending include coral, crystal, decimal, formal, mammal, mineral, postal. Words with the -il ending include basil, evil, nostril, pupil, tendril.	**Writing AF8** Use correct spelling	200–203
Think of a word ending -ar; Think of a word ending -re; Think of a word ending -our; Double trouble	**6. Word structure and spelling** Spell unfamiliar words using known conventions including phoneme/grapheme correspondences and morphological rules	**Think of a word ending -ar. Think of a word ending -re** and **Think of a word ending -our** develop the children's ability to read and spell high-frequency words and to learn conventions that will help them to spell other, less familiar, words using analogy. A useful rule is that -er is a much more common ending than -ar, -re or -our; also words with the -our ending that sounds like -er are usually nouns (an exception is the verb labour). The extension activity on page 207 focuses on using -our as a suffix to form nouns from adjectives and verbs. There are very few of these. Words with the -ar ending include cellar, dollar, popular, regular. **Double trouble** helps the children to learn spelling conventions that will help them to spell unfamiliar words: for example a vowel followed by a consonant and then e is usually a long vowel. They learn to spell these words using known conventions, including grapheme-phoneme correspondence and morphological rules. The sentences help them to use context to select from a choice of pronunciation and spelling alternatives. It is useful to remind them of their previous learning; for example, a double consonant before -el, -e, -er, -ed or the final vowel syllable -a usually makes the vowel short, as in bitter, comma, label, spanner, stopped. A double s usually represents the /s/ phoneme, whereas a single s can represent /z/ (present). Show the children other two-syllable words with the /l/ phoneme following a short vowel. This is usually represented by double f, such as in bluffed, coffee, coffin, differ, duffel, fluffy, giraffe, offer, paraffin, raffle, scuffed, scuffle, sniffing, stiffen, suffix, toffee. Where there is a single f the preceding vowel is usually long, such as in prefix, rifle, trifle, wafer.	**Writing AF8** Use correct spelling	204–206; 207
Word-builder; Odd one out: 1 and 2; Flower power	**6. Word structure and spelling** Recognise a range of prefixes and suffixes, understanding how they modify meaning and spelling, and how they assist in decoding long, complex words	**Word-builder** develops the children's knowledge of a range of prefixes and suffixes and their understanding of how they modify spellings. Possible answers include angry, angered, angering, angers, angrily; brighten, brightens, brightening, brighter, brightly, brightness, brightened; cheerful, cheering, cheers, cheered, cheery, cheerily, cheerless, cheerfulness, cheerlessness; covers, covered, covering; uncover, uncovers, uncovered, uncovering; discover, discovers, discovered, discovery; discovering; recover, recovers, recovered, recovery; recovering; digests, digested, digestion, digesting; indigestion, undigested; enjoys, enjoyed, enjoying, enjoyment; excites, excited, exciting, unexciting; forgives, forgiven, forgiving, unforgiving, forgiveness; decided, decidedly, deciding, decision, indecision, undecided; kinder, kindness, kindly, unkind, unkindness, unkindly; politeness, politely, impoliteness, impolite. **Odd one out: 1** and **2** develop and consolidate the children's knowledge of a range of prefixes and their understanding of how they modify spellings. They learn to identify prefixes and to recognise when the graphemes that make them up are not acting as a prefix. **Flower power** develops the children's knowledge of a range of prefixes and suffixes and their understanding of how they modify spellings. They also have the opportunity to create compound words. They use their knowledge of prefixes and suffixes to help them to generate new words. Possible answers include import, imported, imports, importing; important, importantly; exports, exporting, exported; report, reported, reporting; support, supported, supports, supporting; transport, transports, transported, transporting; airport, seaport, porter; inside, outside; sideways, aside, reside, resident, sideshow, sideline; joyful, joy, enjoy, enjoys, enjoyed, enjoying, enjoyment, joyfully.	**Writing AF8** Use correct spelling	208; 209–210; 211
Writing riddles; Limerick writer	**9. Creating and shaping texts** Use layout, format, graphics and illustrations for different purposes	**Writing riddles** helps the children to play with words and ideas to create riddles that involve homophones and descriptions. They learn some new technical language. **Limerick writer** provides a format to help the children to write their own limericks modelled on those they have read. They could first listen to some limericks and clap or tap the rhythm of the syllables and count the number of syllables in each line. Point out that limericks tell a story and help the children to find the verbs in the past tense. To help them to appreciate the structure of limericks you could print some and cut out each line separately, then ask the children to put them in order. Help them to identify the criteria for success so that they can use them to evaluate their writing: the correct number of syllables and the appropriate rhyming lines.	All Writing AFs, especially: **Writing AF1** Write imaginative, interesting and thoughtful texts; **Writing AF2** Produce texts which are appropriate to task, reader and purpose; **Writing AF7** Select appropriate and effective vocabulary	212; 213
Sentences in poems	**11. Sentence structure and punctuation** Compose sentences using adjectives, verbs and nouns for precision, clarity and impact	**Sentences in poems** develops the children's appreciation that poems can be written in sentences but that some are not. They identify the lines of poetry which make up a sentence and those which do not. During the plenary session, ask them why the parts which are not sentences are included in poems. Draw out that poets use words to create effects as well as to tell the reader something and that these effects help to communicate feelings and to create an atmosphere and mood (humour, excitement, sadness and so on). Also note that sentences in poems do not always end with a full stop and that sometimes they can extend over several lines – even over an entire verse.	**Writing AF5** Vary sentences for clarity, purpose and effect; **Writing AF6** Write with technical accuracy of syntax and punctuation in phrases, clauses and sentences	214

Ban the gum?

- **What do you think about banning chewing gum?**
- **Why?**
- **Write notes.**
- **Plan what you would say about chewing gum.**

I think chewing gum should be banned because	I don't think chewing gum should be banned because

NOW TRY THIS!

- **Give a talk about what you think.**

Use your voice.
Use your face.
Use your hands.
Think about how to stand, sit and move.

Teachers' note Ask the children to think about whether chewing gum should be banned. They could complete the page as a group, collating everyone's thoughts, or they could make notes on their own thoughts about chewing gum. Remind them to say why they think as they do: what makes them dislike chewing gum or what makes them think it is all right.

- **Work with a partner.**
- **Ask your partner this question:**

> **Should children be given pocket money?**

- **Listen to the answer.**
- **Ask your partner other questions to find out more.**

(Why?)   (How?)   (What would you do?)   (Why do you think that?)

- **Listen to the answers.**
- **Then write notes on what your partner says.**

What my partner thinks and why

_____

_____

_____

_____

_____

_____

_____

_____

NOW TRY THIS!

- **Tell your group about your partner's views.**

Teachers' note Introduce this activity by modelling an interview in which you try to find out what someone thinks about a different topic. Ask the children to notice the questions you ask and how they encourage the other person to say more. Use this with 'Pocket money: 2' or you could use the CD-ROM to change the topic in the speech bubble. Provide some information on the new topic.

A Lesson for Every Day
Literacy
7-8 Years
© A&C Black

Pocket money: 2

Pocket money is a small amount of money that parents agree to give their children each week to buy treats.

It's a weekly gift.

Thank you.

Pocket money does not have to be earned.

Having pocket money helps children to learn about saving.

We cannot afford to give our children pocket money.

We wouldn't know what the children are buying. They could buy anything.

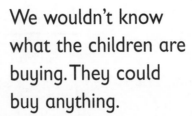

BEER

Having pocket money helps children to learn what things cost.

Children should earn any money they have.

The average weekly pocket money for 7 to 10 year olds in the UK is £2.00.

I prefer to give children money when they need to buy something.

NOTE BOOK

NOW TRY THIS!

• **Write some other ideas about pocket money.**

Teachers' note See 'Pocket money: 1'. The children should read the information on this page before they begin their discussions. Or you could ask only those being questioned to read it and the others to find out more by asking questions. Afterwards, ask the ones who listened to and questioned their partners what they learned from listening.

A Lesson for Every Day
Literacy
7–8 Years
© A&C Black

Mystery story

- **Read the story opening.**
- **What might the secret message mean?**

Work in a group of four.

Chapter 1 The Chimney

The builders had gone home by the time Jaz got back from school. A layer of dust had settled on the cupboard in the hall, on the phone, on the tops of the family photos. She could taste the plaster.

She pushed the living room door open. The room was empty – bare floorboards, no curtains, a light bulb hanging from the ceiling. There was a great hole where the old gas fire used to be. Jaz's mother had been right – there must have been an enormous fireplace here once.

She looked up into the chimney. Then Dan came in from school. "Looking for skeletons?" he asked. "People used to hide all sorts of stuff up chimneys before they blocked them up: old shoes, newspapers, even bodies."

"Don't be si …" She stopped, blinking up at something in the darkness, and pulled a rusty tin down from a ledge in the chimney. She put it on the dusty floor and lifted the lid. Inside was a necklace of green glass beads and a scroll of paper tied with a green ribbon.

"Let's see!" said Dan. They unrolled the paper:

> *Sarah Griffiths hid these on the 6th day of April 1861. If they are here after I die the finder keeps. Beware the curse of green.*

- **Write everyone's ideas on the spider chart.**

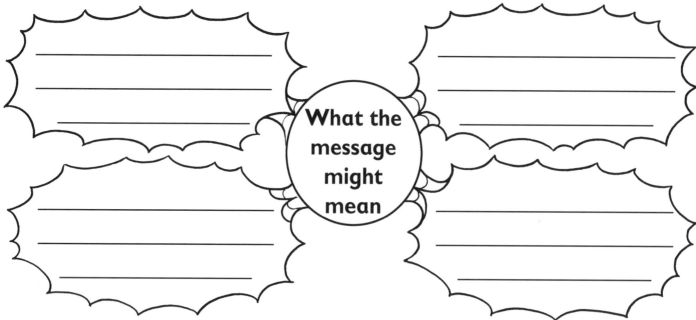

What the message might mean

- **Discuss each idea. Do you agree or disagree?**

Teachers' note The children could begin by reading the story opening to themselves or with a partner: for example, a low-attaining reader with a confident reader or a pair who both need some help, to support one another. Groups of four can then discuss what the message might mean, note all the ideas on the spider chart and say whether they agree or disagree.

A Lesson for Every Day
Literacy
7–8 Years
© A&C Black

Memory tree

- **What does your group remember about a story you have read?**
- **Take turns to speak.**
- **Listen to one another.**
- **Then write notes.**

Add something to what the others say or say something different.

Story title _____

Author _____

Name _____

Name _____

Name _____

Name _____

NOW TRY THIS!

- **Share your memories with another group.**

Teachers' note You could use an example of your own (where a discussion helped you and others to remember a story, film or television programme you had all read or seen) to model how listening to others can help us to remember a shared experience. Remind the children that everyone should be encouraged to speak and that they should listen to one another.

Character chat

- **What does your group think about a story character?**
- **Take turns to speak.**
- **Listen to one another.**
- **Then write notes.**

> Work in a group.

Story title _____

Author _____

Character _____

_____ thinks _____

_____

_____

_____ thinks _____

_____

_____

_____

_____ thinks _____

_____

_____

_____ thinks _____

_____

> **NOW TRY THIS!**

- **Share your views with another group.**

Teachers' note Invite other adults to help you to model how listening to others can help us to remember a story, television or film character. Remind the children to encourage everyone to speak and listen to one another. The class could share their ideas on the interactive whiteboard and agree what was good and what was bad about the character or what they liked or disliked about him or her.

A Lesson for Every Day
Literacy
7-8 Years
© A&C Black

Pass it on

- **Work in a group of four.**
- **Read a verse each and pass on the smile.**

A Smile

Smiling is infectious
you catch it like the flu.
When someone smiled at me today
I started smiling too.

I passed around a corner
and someone saw my grin.
When he smiled, I realized
I'd passed it on to him.

I thought about my smile and then
I realized its worth.
A single smile like mine could travel
right around the earth.

If you feel a smile begin
don't leave it undetected.
Let's start a epidemic quick
and get the world infected.

Jez Alborough

- **How did the poem make you feel? Can you make people feel happy by smiling at them? If you feel sad, might this make people around you feel sad?**

Discuss this with your group.

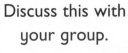

- **Share your group's thoughts with the rest of the class**

NOW TRY THIS!

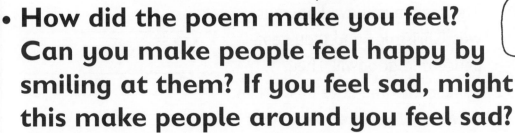

- **Take turns to pass on an expression:**

| excitement | being bored | being tired |

Teachers' note To introduce this activity, tell the children that they are going to read a poem with their group and then discuss how it makes them feel. Ask the children if they can think of times when their feelings and actions have been influenced by the moods or emotions of people around them.

A Lesson for Every Day
Literacy
7–8 Years
© A&C Black

The sea: 1

- **What is the** atmosphere **like?**

- **Write a word from the work-bank.**
- **What might happen?**
- **Write notes.**

He looked out at the stormy sea where his father was sailing, every day coming nearer home, and on that wild water he saw only mist and spray, and the cruel waves dashing over jagged splinters of rock.

The seas must have known it was Christmas and they kept peace and goodwill. They danced into the cove in sparkling waves, and fluttered their flags of white foam, and tossed their treasures of seaweed and shells.

Teachers' note Use this with 'The sea: 2'. Tell the children that these descriptions are from different points in the same story. Ask them about the atmosphere: calm, scary, exciting, threatening and so on. Encourage them to give evidence from the text. What kind of action might happen here?

A Lesson for Every Day
Literacy
7–8 Years
© **A&C Black**

The sea: 2

The water was deep blue, like the sky, and purple shadows hovered over it, as the waves gently rocked the cormorants fishing there.

_____
_____
_____
_____

From his bedroom window he could watch the great waves with their curling plumes of white foam, and count the seagulls as they circled in the blue sky.

_____
_____
_____

_____
_____
_____
_____

The wintry sun made a pathway on the water, flickering with points of light on the crests of the waves.

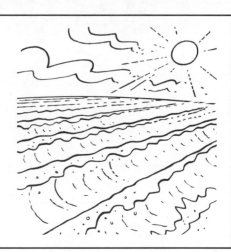

These passages are from *The Fairy Ship* by Alison Uttley.

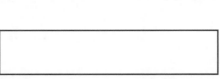 **NOW TRY THIS!**

- **Choose a description of the sea.**
- **Write two or three sentences about what happens next.**

Teachers' note Continued from 'The sea: 1'. Ask the children to read each description with a partner, to imagine the scene and to think about what the characters might be doing or thinking about. They can then make notes about their ideas, to share during the plenary session.

A Lesson for Every Day
Literacy
7–8 Years
© A&C Black

Settings match

- **Write what you would see and hear in each** `setting` **.**
- **Match the story outlines to the settings.**

_____

_____

_____

_____

_____

_____

| Rosie makes friends with children from the 1930s. | Ben finds dragon's egg. Keeps it in kitchen cupboard. |
| Alien takes the form of a dog and brings a strange message. | Mr Hogg hates children, hates mess, but he changes. |

Teachers' note Remind the children of books they have read in which the setting was described in some detail. Discuss how it helped to introduce the story by giving clues as to what might happen or by creating an atmosphere. They could discuss the settings on this page in pairs and decide what type of story might take place.

A Lesson for Every Day
Literacy
7-8 Years
© A&C Black

The flood

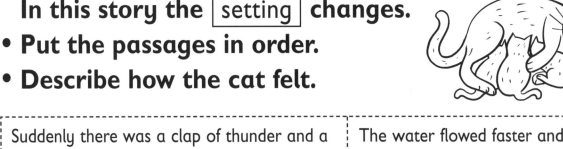

In this story the setting changes.

- Put the passages in order.
- Describe how the cat felt.

Suddenly there was a clap of thunder and a great blast of wind. The door of the shed blew open with a bang. The water rushed in and the box swirled round and round. Then it floated out of the shed into the garden.

_____

_____

_____

The water flowed faster and faster under the door until it was inches deep. Just when Minnie was getting ready to take a kitten in her mouth and spring on to the wheelbarrow, and then on to the shelf, a strange thing happened. The wooden box began to move about. It was floating. It was floating like a boat.

_____

_____

Minnie's eyes shone like green lamps. She could see, under the door of the shed, a trickle of water. The trickle grew into a puddle. The puddle grew into a wave. The wave came nearer across the floor. Then it reached the box in the corner.

_____

_____

_____

One night, when the kittens were fast asleep, curled like furry balls beside their mother, a storm blew up. The door and window of the shed rattled. The rain fell in floods on the roof. There were terrible claps of thunder and bright, zig-zag flashes of lightning.

_____

_____

_____

From *The Ten Tales of Shellover* by Ruth Ainsworth

NOW TRY THIS!

- **Describe the setting before the storm.**
- **How did the cat feel?**

Teachers' note The children could read the passages aloud in groups of four and then co-operate in putting them in the correct order. When children have finished, they could work in groups and do a quick sketch to accompany each extract, to support their sense of the setting and the changes that occur.

A Lesson for Every Day
Literacy
7-8 Years
© A&C Black

The woods

- **Imagine walking into the woods.**
- **Write what you see, hear and feel.**

 Write notes.

_____

_____

_____

_____

_____

_____

 **NOW TRY THIS!**

- **What might happen in each setting?**
- **Write notes.**

Teachers' note Ask the children to imagine stepping into the woods in the first picture. How might they feel? Why? What kind of story might take place there and what might happen? Repeat this for the second picture, then point out that both pictures show the same place – but what is different? How is the atmosphere altered?

A Lesson for Every Day
Literacy
7-8 Years
© A&C Black

Exploring a setting

- **Imagine the scene in the passage.**
- **Continue the description.**

Write what Emil saw, heard, smelled and felt. Write what he did.

Emil turned the handle and pushed the door open with his foot. A clutter of dishes, plates, pans, knives, forks and spoons covered the draining board. Spidery grey lines criss-crossed the surface that was once white. A few old soggy chips poked up through the slimy fat in the brown-spattered chip pan like logs in a swamp. The smell of stale food lay thick in the air. A tap dripped slowly. The water mingled with oil on a cracked plate.

He kicked an empty baked beans tin out of the way and leaned on the door to close it.

_____

_____

_____

_____

_____

_____

NOW TRY THIS!

- **Talk to a friend about what might happen in this setting.**

Teachers' note Ask the children for words to describe the atmosphere in this scene. They could work in groups to list suitable adjectives and then to choose the three or four best ones. They could then continue working in a group to discuss how Emil might feel and what might happen in this scene.

A Lesson for Every Day
Literacy
7–8 Years
© A&C Black

Atmospheric: 1

- **Make a different** atmosphere **in each picture.**
- **Write words to use in a story in these** settings **.**

Draw on the pictures.
Colour them.
Write on the pictures.

'Fun' setting

'Scary' setting

NOW TRY THIS!

- **Write notes about what might happen in each setting.**

Teachers' note The children should realise that the two settings feature the same place but that the different titles ('Fun' setting and 'Scary' setting) make the place look different to the viewer. Their drawings and notes could indicate story characters and events as well as words to describe the settings. Encourage them to use colour to create different atmospheres.

A Lesson for Every Day
Literacy
7–8 Years
© A&C Black

Atmospheric: 2

- **Talk to a friend about what might happen in each** `setting` **.**
- **Write your ideas on the story plans.**

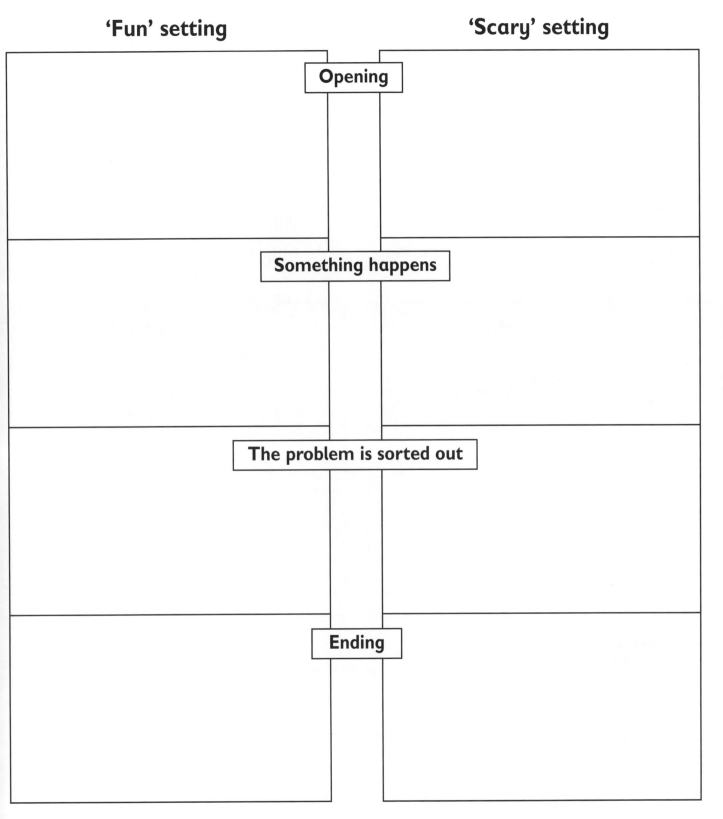

'Fun' setting   'Scary' setting

Opening

Something happens

The problem is sorted out

Ending

Teachers' note The children will need to look at their pictures and notes from 'Atmospheric: 1'. It is useful to discuss with them how the description of a setting can set the scene for an event and prepare the reader for it. The pictures could be used on separate occasions as starting points for planning the outlines of different stories.

- **Choose words for a story in each** [setting] .
- **Write them on the notepads.**

Word-bank

bare	crept	glide	lurked	skipped
bright	dank	gloomy	oozed	slimy
cheerfully	dark	grasped	played	sly
chirping	dismal	grim	rattled	smiled
clanked	eerie	joked	scampering	snarled
clouds	flowers	jolly	shivered	sprang
comical	fluttered	laughed	silly	sunny
creepy	glad	lively	singing	terror

'Fun' setting

'Scary' setting

NOW TRY THIS!

- **Write three sentences to describe each setting.**
- **Write three sentences about what happened there.**

Think about the kind of story that might happen there. Use your story plan.

Teachers' note The children will need to look at their pictures and notes from 'Atmospheric: 1 and 2'. Different groups could work on different types of story: 'fun' or 'scary'. They should think of the connotations of the words and of their effects to decide whether they help to create a 'fun' or 'scary' atmosphere.

A Lesson for Every Day
Literacy
7–8 Years
© A&C Black

Words for describing

These words describe someone or something.

tall round sad wavy long soft hot

In sentences they describe **nouns** .

• **Circle the words that describe the** nouns .

1 There was a tall green plant growing beside the small cottage .

2 An angry woman was shaking her fist at her young son .

3 The frightened lad began to climb up the enormous plant .

4 "The cow was old. This beanstalk is wonderful," he said.

5 He looked up and saw a pair of huge boots .

6 The huge boots were on a pair of gigantic feet on the ends of two massive legs .

NOW TRY THIS!

• **Write two sentences to continue the story.**
• **Underline the nouns.**
• **Add a word to describe each noun.**

Teachers' note Remind the children of the different purposes of words in a sentence: to name people or things (or to use instead of these names), to show actions, to say where, when or why things happened and to show belonging. Tell them that they are going to investigate words which describe things, people and places. Emphasise that these words describe nouns.

A Lesson for Every Day
Literacy
7-8 Years
© A&C Black

Describe and draw

- **Complete the sentence. Use two words from the adjective-bank.**

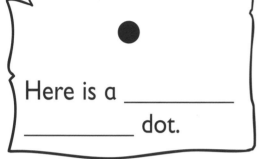

Here is a _____ _____ dot.

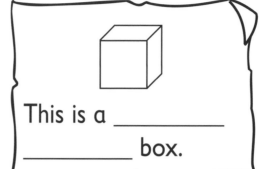

This is a _____ _____ box.

This shows a _____ _____ line.

Here we have a _____ _____ cat.

Here you can see two _____ _____ ducks.

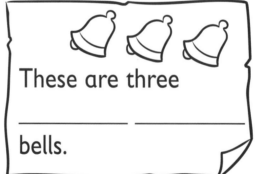

These are three _____ _____ bells.

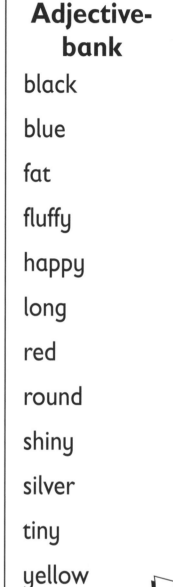

Adjective-bank

black

blue

fat

fluffy

happy

long

red

round

shiny

silver

tiny

yellow

NOW TRY THIS!

- **Write adjectives in the gaps.**

A _____ smell drifted through the _____ window. A _____ sound came from the _____ frying pan. Then I saw six _____ sausages.

Teachers' note Remind the children of their previous learning about words that describe and explain that these are called adjectives. Ask them to choose the most appropriate describing word for the nouns in the captions. Provide colouring pencils/crayons for the children to colour in the artwork to match the adjective.

A Lesson for Every Day
Literacy
7–8 Years
© A&C Black

- **Read the poem to yourself.**
- **Think about it so that you can discuss it with your group.**
- **Write some notes in the boxes.**

**The Real Story
(But Don't Tell the Tiny Kids!)**

Jack and Jill went up the hill,

To paint a water colour.

Jack loves things bright, like summer light;

Jill likes them rather duller.

They did no good: they never could

Agree on how to do it.

Jill said, "Today, do what I say!

What's that? You won't? I knew it!"

He turned and smiled. That made her wild.

She stamped and shook and shouted.

He wasn't cowed; he laughed out loud,

And that's how he got clouted.

She knocked him down, and broke his crown,

Then ran to fetch a doctor.

Jack lay in bed, with bandaged head,

And thought, "I wish I'd socked her!"

Alan Hayward

NOW TRY THIS!

- **See if you can find anything that Jack or Jill said or did that was right.**
- **Underline these.**

Teachers' note The children could plan how to read the poem aloud as well as considering its message about how to disagree politely without falling out. Ask them to think about how Jack and Jill discussed their views about painting and what they did right or wrong. They should make notes individually in the boxes on this page.

A Lesson for Every Day
Literacy
7-8 Years
© A&C Black

43

Jack and Jill: 2

- **How could Jack and Jill get on better?**
- **Talk about it with your group.**
- **Write notes on what you all agree.**

(Verse 1 notes have been done for you.)

Everyone should speak.
Everyone should listen.

Verse 1 _J & J like different types of colour. OK to have different likes._
OK to disagree. Need to agree how to paint picture.

Verse 2 _____

Verse 3 _____

Verse 4 _____

NOW TRY THIS!

Work with your group.

- **How can talking together help to stop fights?**
- **Write three sentences to tell the class.**

44

Teachers' note Use this with the poem on 'Jack and Jill: 1. You could use the completed section to model how to write notes. The children should complete this page as a group, making notes on what Jack and Jill could have done and said to share their different views without falling out. They could then share their ideas with other groups.

A Lesson for Every Day
Literacy
7-8 Years
© A&C Black

Jack and Jill: 3

- **Write sentences to use in a voicemail message to Jack and Jill.**
- **Explain how they can plan what to do without getting angry.**
- **Use your notes to help.**
- **Record your message.**

Work with your group.
Everyone should speak.
Everyone should listen.

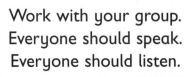

_____

_____

_____

_____

_____

_____

_____

_____

_____

NOW TRY THIS!

- **Tell the new story of Jack and Jill painting.**
- **Show how they can disagree politely and plan what to do.**

Teachers' note The children should first have completed 'Jack and Jill: 1 and 2'. Show them how to use their notes to write complete sentences to use in a voicemail message. Provide cassette recorders so they can record their messages to Jack and Jill and discuss which ones are the most persuasive. The children could also enact Jack and Jill listening to and discussing the message.

Jack and Jill: 4

- **Write a new Jack and Jill poem.**
- **This time they disagree politely and plan what to do.**
- **Write a new title.**

Title _____

(_____)

> Work with your group.
> Everyone should speak.
> Everyone should listen.

Jack and Jill went up the hill,

To paint a water colour.

Jack loves things bright, like summer light;

Jill likes them rather duller.

_____

_____

_____

_____

_____

_____

_____

_____

_____

_____

_____

NOW TRY THIS!

- **Take turns to read a verse aloud.**

Teachers' note The children should first have completed 'Jack and Jill: 1–3'. This could be used in conjunction with work in creating and shaping texts in which the children use a poem as a model for their own. However, they should change the poem on 'Jack and Jill: 1' to tell the story of Jack and Jill discussing their different views without a quarrel. Approach this as a shared writing activity.

A Lesson for Every Day
Literacy
7-8 Years
© A&C Black

- **Read the poem aloud.**
- **Talk about how to make it grow louder ... then become quieter again. You could do this by using more and more voices ... then fewer and fewer voices.**

Work with a group.

Windy Nights

Whenever the moon and stars are set,

Whenever the wind is high,

All night long in the dark and wet,

   A man goes riding by.

Late in the night when the fires are out,

   Why does he gallop and gallop about?

Whenever the trees are crying aloud,

   And ships are tossed at sea,

By, on the highway, low and loud,

   By at the gallop goes he.

By at the gallop he goes, and then

   By he comes back at the gallop again.

Robert Louis Stevenson

Readers

_____

_____

_____

_____

_____

_____

_____

_____

_____

_____

_____

NOW TRY THIS!

- **Read the poem aloud to another group using your plan.**
- **Ask them what was good about it.**
- **Ask if any changes would help.**

Teachers' note The children should first read the poem to themselves, then agree in their groups on how it should be read aloud. You could play a sound recording of a rough sea breaking on a shore and help the children to notice the 'coming and going' movement and sound. Point out that the rider, too, comes and goes and help them to find a way of reading the poem that will reflect this.

A Lesson for Every Day
Literacy
7-8 Years
© A&C Black

- **Discuss the 'buzz points' with your group.**
- **Wait for everyone to have their say.**
- **Then write what the group agrees:** yes or no .

The poem was written a long time ago.

There is a calm feeling in the poem.

There is a mystery about the man.

There is a lot of fast movement in the poem.

It is a very quiet poem.

It makes us picture a brightly-lit scene.

The man is looking for someone or something.

NOW TRY THIS!

- **Use your answers to help you to plan a talk about the poem.**

Work together. Decide who will say what.

Teachers' note This introduces 'buzz points' as points to discuss in connection with a poem, story or topic. Use it with 'Windy nights: 1' to help the children to discuss their responses to the poem 'Windy Nights'.

A Lesson for Every Day
Literacy
7–8 Years
© A&C Black

Persephone and the seasons

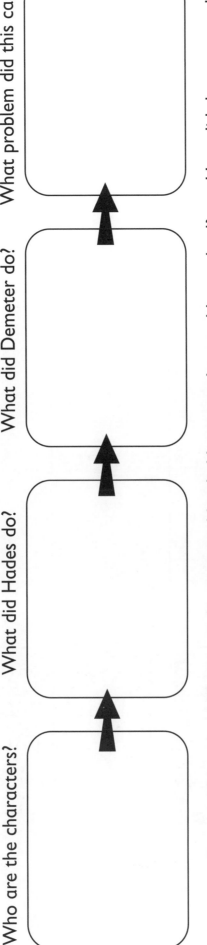

- Read the story of Persephone.
- On the story map, write notes about the main events.

| Who are the characters? | What did Hades do? | What did Demeter do? | What problem did this cause? |

| What was Zeus's solution? | What was the next problem? | How was that problem solved? | How did the story end? |

Use your notes to help.

- Tell the story of Persephone with a friend.

Teachers' note The children should first have read the story of Persephone. You could help them to compare it with the main events in other myths: in King Midas it is a wish, but in Persephone a dramatic event leads to a quest. Children should cut out the two rows as two strips and glue them end to end in sequence.

A Lesson for Every Day
Literacy
7–8 Years
© A&C Black

The quest

Title _____

Name of hero or heroine _____

> Think about places, people, spells, charms, clothing…

Settings

On land	
Underground	
In the air	

Dangers

Animals	
People	
Nature	

Keeping safe

Charms	
Clothing	
Spells	

NOW TRY THIS!

- What was the greatest danger? Why?
- Write about how the hero or heroine survived this.

Teachers' note Use this to help the children to describe a quest myth they have read. Focus on the setting of the myth, the perils facing the main character (for example, the actions of the gods, monsters and so on) and how he or she keeps safe (for example, a protective spell, garment or amulet).

A Lesson for Every Day
Literacy
7-8 Years
© A&C Black

Character and quest

- **Work with a friend.**
- **Choose a** character **for a** quest .
- **Choose an object that your character has to find.**

What has happened before your story begins? Where does the character have to go?

Characters

Decimus, a Roman boy in Britain long ago.

Fawzia, a modern girl in any big city you know.

Kieran, a boy who has travelled into the future.

Elesa, a girl who has come to Earth from another planet.

Objects

A golden sword.

A fine silk scarf with silver threads that has no weight at all.

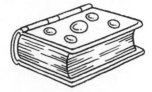

A leather-bound, jewel-studded book of the wisest things ever written.

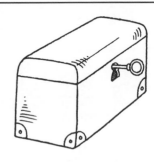

A box of secrets.

- **Talk about why the character has to find this object.**
- **Write notes about your ideas.**

Notes

Teachers' note After choosing their character the children should work in pairs to discuss his or her background and then decide on an object that the character has to search for. They should also come up with a reason why the object is so important and what will happen when it has been found.

Quest game

- **Play in a group of four.**
- **Roll the die and move your counter.**
- **To finish you must land on the Chest of Promises.**

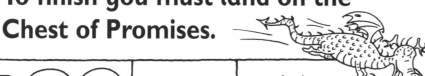

You need

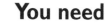 a die

four counters

quest cards

Opening

Take a quest card.

A dragon attacks. Go back to the opening.

Elves disguised as owls send you the wrong way. Miss a turn.

Take a quest card.

Take a quest card.

You fall into a swamp. Miss a turn.

Forest of Fear

A wizard turns you into a snail. Go back three.

Sea of Dreams

Lost in a maze. Miss a turn.

Mountain of Mystery

Valley of Flowers

You fall into a pit. Miss two turns.

Calming Clouds

Take a quest card.

The Dog of Doom attacks. Go back six.

Take a quest card.

The Battle of the Robots. Miss a turn.

Lake of Legends

The Spirit of the Evil Monster finds you. Go back three.

Ending

Chest of Promises

Trolls ambush you. Go back two.

You lose your shadow. Miss a turn.

Crater of Cares

NOW TRY THIS!

- **Tell the story of your quest to a friend.**

Teachers' note This could be used in conjunction with the character and object chosen on 'Character and quest' or as a separate activity to generate ideas for a quest story. Use it with the cards on 'Quest cards'. Remind the children of quest stories they have read and discuss the challenges faced by the main character during the quest: evil characters, physical danger, difficult journeys and so on. See 'Quest cards'.

A Lesson for Every Day
Literacy
7–8 Years
© A&C Black

Quest cards

- **Cut out the cards and put them in a pile face down.**
- **Pick up a card when you land on 'Take a quest card'.**

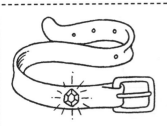
Wear the Magic Belt and dragons cannot harm you.

The Ring of Truth overcomes all robots.

Magical Meat keeps the Dog of Doom chewing. He cannot harm you.

The winged horse can take you away from any troubles.

The Turquoise Stone protects you from magic spells.

No one can see you when you wear the Helmet of Invisibility.

Take the King's Sword and you will never lose a battle.

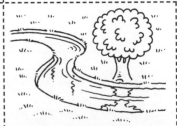
Swim in the River of Eternity and nothing can harm you.

The Captain's Compass will never let you get lost.

The Four Winds will take you away from any danger.

The Woven Headband keeps away all evil creatures.

The Sorcerer's Spectacles find anything you lose.

Wear the Golden Gown and nothing can harm you.

Carry the Royal Rock to ward off evil.

Strike fear into elves with the Lance of the Lambdas.

The Eagle of Evermore will save you from all harm.

Teachers' note Use these with 'Quest game'. A story character could be given or could win (in a battle or one-to-one combat) an object that will be useful during the quest: for example, for protection from evil or physical harm, to help with difficult tasks or to overcome enemies.

A Lesson for Every Day
Literacy
7-8 Years
© A&C Black

Quest route

- **Choose three** [settings] **for your** [quest].
- **Who lives there? What happens there?**
- **Write** [notes].
- **Draw a line to join the notes to the place.**

The planet Luminid

Characters	What happens
_____	_____
_____	_____
Special object	_____
_____	

Characters	
_____	
_____	
Special object	
_____	
What happens	
_____	

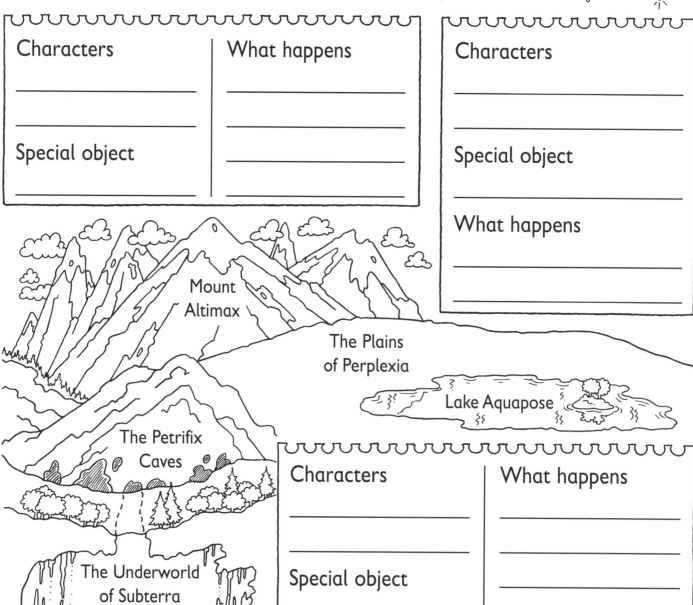

Mount Altimax

The Plains of Perplexia

Lake Aquapose

The Petrifix Caves

The Underworld of Subterra

Characters	What happens
_____	_____
_____	_____
Special object	_____
_____	

NOW TRY THIS!

- **Work with a friend.**
- **Act what happens in one setting.**

Teachers' note Copy this onto A3 paper. It is useful to point out the places that could be settings during the quest before asking the children to talk to a friend about what might happen there and what the main character in the story might do or find there. These could be linked with the activities on 'Character and quest', 'Quest game' and 'Quest route'.

A Lesson for Every Day
Literacy
7–8 Years
© A&C Black

The Chest of Promises

- **What is in the Chest of Promises? Write on the chest.**
- **Where is it?**
- **How does your character find it?**
- **Who or what is guarding it?**
- **Write on the notepads.**

The setting	Finding the chest	The guard(s)

NOW TRY THIS!

- **Tell the story of how your character finds the chest, beats the guard(s) and opens it.**

Work with a friend.

Teachers' note Ask the children to imagine what promises might be in the chest. Tell them that their story character has set off on a quest to search for, and collect, the chest but that he or she has to overcome many challenges on the way, including whatever or whoever is guarding the chest. They could plan a story around this and suggest ideas about how the promises affect the characters.

A Lesson for Every Day
Literacy
7-8 Years
© A&C Black

On your screen

- **Read the words on the screen.**
- **Write the sentences.**

Don't forget the full stops and capital letters.

the wind became stronger it was blowing me back but I had to reach the other side of the beach sprays of sand dashed on to my face I kept my mouth tightly closed my eyes hurt there was sand in my mouth then my foot struck something hard it felt like metal

- **What might happen next?**
- **Write a sentence.**

Teachers' note Give the children a copy of this page and ask them to follow the passage as you read it. Read it without pausing at the ends of sentences. Read the final sentence as if there is something to follow. Ask the children if they think it sounded right. What was wrong with it? Why do you read it like that and how does punctuation help? Model this with the first sentence.

A Lesson for Every Day
Literacy
7-8 Years
© A&C Black

Past and present: 1

The ⟨past⟩ has happened.

The ⟨present⟩ is happening now.

In the ⟨past⟩ I ⟨was⟩ a baby.

At ⟨present⟩ I ⟨am⟩ eight years old.

- **Fill in the gaps.**

Past	Present
I lived in Wales.	I _____ in England.
I _____ to nursery.	I go to school.
I liked my teddy.	I _____ my computer.
I _____ a tricycle.	I ride a bike.
I slept in a cot.	I _____ in a bed.
I _____ from a bottle.	I drink from a cup.
I _____ with rattles.	I play with toy cars.
I ate baby food.	I _____ all kinds of food.
I had no teeth.	I _____ a lot of teeth.
I _____ a baby gro.	I wear jeans.

NOW TRY THIS!

- **Write three sentences about these:**

schools in the past

schools in the present

Teachers' note Remind the children that we change the words for what we do depending on whether we are doing it now or have already done it. If appropriate, introduce the term verb for these words. You could link this with word-level work on adding the suffix -ed and on how words change according to meaning.

A Lesson for Every Day
Literacy
7-8 Years
© A&C Black

Past and present: 2

The | past | was happening.
The | present | is happening now.

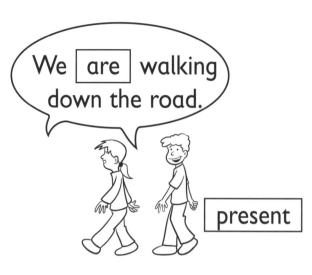

We | are | walking
down the road.

present

We | were | walking
down the road.

past

- **Write these sentences in the present tense.**
- **Circle the words you changed.**

1 I was eating my breakfast.

_____

2 We were going to town.

_____

3 He was looking for his coat.

_____

4 They were sitting at the table.

_____

5 You were riding Henry's bike.

_____

6 Dad was reading a story.

_____

NOW TRY THIS!

- **Write two sentences about what you are doing now.**
- **Write them in the past tense.**

Teachers' note Remind the children of their previous learning about the past tenses of verbs and introduce the use of auxiliary verbs like *am, is, are, was* and *were* for forming the present and past tenses: *I am talking, You were singing* and so on. You could link this with word-level work on adding the suffix *-ing*.

A Lesson for Every Day
Literacy
7–8 Years
© A&C Black

One thing after another

- **Circle the words that tell you the order in which things happened.**

Leah had to get through the Golden Door, but before that she had to pass the dragon that guarded it. Before she could get near the dragon it sensed that she was there. She hoped that the spell of protection had not worn off. After a few minutes the dragon turned away. This was her chance. She pointed the Stillit at the dragon's head. It worked instantly. The dragon was still.

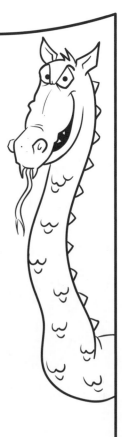

Now Leah had to check what was on the other side of the door. First she pressed her ear to the door and listened. Not a sound. Then she turned the key and pushed. The door didn't budge. She pushed harder. It still didn't budge. Her next thought was that it was bolted. In a few seconds she was sliding her very fine sword through the tiny gaps around the door. She had to be quick. Before long the Merfolk would catch up with her. After what seemed like hours the sword caught on something. In a flash Leah pushed the bolt-mover through the tiny gap and moved it backwards and forwards. It took about thirty seconds to free the bolt. As soon as it had moved, she pulled the door with all her might. Straight away she knew why the door had been locked and bolted.

NOW TRY THIS!

- **Write about what you have done today.**
- **Show the order in which you did everything.**

Teachers' note Tell the children that they are going to read a passage from a story and that their task is to look for words which tell them in what order the events in the passage happened. They can then reread the passage, with a partner if appropriate, and circle these words.

A Lesson for Every Day
Literacy
7–8 Years
© A&C Black

Because

You can join two sentences with | because | .

- **Draw a line from a cloud to a flower to join the sentences.**
- **Write** | because | **on the line.**
- **Write the long sentences.**

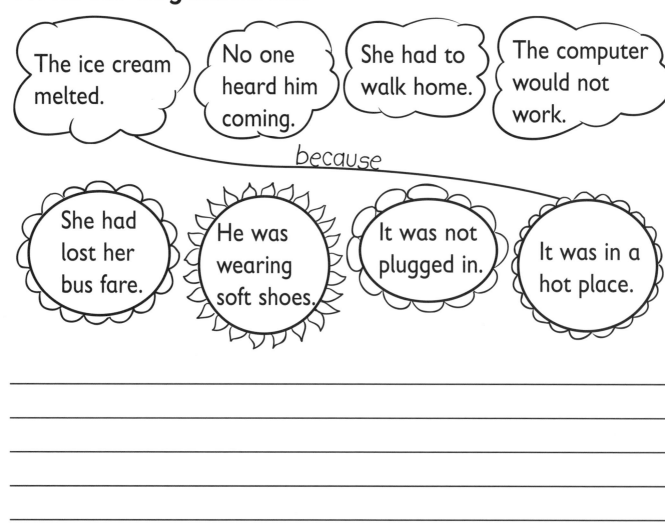

_____

_____

_____

_____

_____

_____

_____

NOW TRY THIS!

- **Write another** | because | **sentence.**
- **Split it into two shorter sentences.**

Teachers' note Remind the children of their previous work on words used for joining sentences in order to make one long sentence. Ask for examples of such words: for example, *and*, *but*. Point out that sometimes part of a sentence says why something was done. Introduce the word *because* for joining two sentences where one says *why* something happens.

A Lesson for Every Day
Literacy
7–8 Years
© A&C Black

That's why

A sentence can say why something is done.

Put your jacket on so that you won't be cold.

• **Write a** why **ending for these sentences.**

1 Look and listen for traffic _in case_ _____

_____ .

2 I shall lock my bike _____

_____ .

3 She put an umbrella in her bag _____

_____ .

4 They went to town _____

_____ .

5 You must buy a parking ticket _____

_____ .

6 They went into the café _____

_____ .

NOW TRY THIS!

• **Write three sentences about why you do things.**
• **Use words from the word-bank.**

Teachers' note Remind the children of their previous work on the use of *because* to join sentences to say why something happened. Ask for examples of other words which say *why* (see the word-bank).

A Lesson for Every Day
Literacy
7-8 Years
© A&C Black

61

The middle of the night, and everyone in the house asleep. Everyone? Then what was that noise?

Creak! And then, after a pause, *Creak!* And then, *Creak!*

Mrs Sparrow heard it. The noise woke her, as the crying of her children would have woken her. But this was someone else's job. She nudged her husband… She nudged and nudged until Bill Sparrow stirred, groaned. He had been dreaming of the garden…

"Bill!" she whispered. "Come on! Wake up!"

"Yes," he said. "Just a minute, and I'll do that."

"Listen."

Creak! And then *Creak!* And then, *Creak!*

"Can't you hear it?"

"Yes."

"What is it?"

"I don't know."

"But it's in the house!"

"Yes, it is!"

"Downstairs!"

"Yes."

CREAK!

"Bill! What are you going to do about it?"

He nearly said again, "I don't know." Then he pulled himself together. He tried hard to think clearly what he ought to do. First, he ought to wake up properly. Then, he ought to get up. He ought to find out what was making the noise that bothered Alice so. That was it: find out.

"I'm getting up," he said aloud. "I'm going to find out about that row downstairs."

He reached for the pencil-torch that Mrs Sparrow kept under the pillow. He wouldn't switch on the lights; he wouldn't even use the torch until he had to. He would surprise whatever it was. *Whoever* it was.

From *The Battle of Bubble and Squeak* by Philippa Pearce

Teachers' note The children begin by reading the passage to themselves or with a partner: for example, a low-attaining reader with a confident reader or a pair who both need some help supporting one another. They then talk to their groups about how to read each part of the story. They could use tape recorders or MP3 players to record their readings for evaluating and changing.

A Lesson for Every Day
Literacy
7-8 Years
© A&C Black

A noise in the night: 2

• **Plan how to read the story aloud.**

Think about how to use your voice…

…how loud

…voices for different characters…

…a voice for the narrator…

…the pitch: high or low…

…the mood: serious, funny, nervous, worried, excited and so on…

…tone of voice: telling, asking, exclaiming, wondering…

Voices:	Other sounds:
1 _____	1 _____
2 _____	2 _____
3 _____	3 _____

Dialogue: Key to underlined words

worried or nervous

sleepy

loud

whispered

_____

calm

impatient

high

low or gruff

_____

Use different colours to show how to read the spoken words.

Useful sound effects I could make

_____

_____

_____

_____

_____

_____

NOW TRY THIS!

• **Read the story using your notes to help with expression.**

Teachers' note Use this page to help the children to focus on how to read with expression – what expression will help and how to change their voices: for example, to indicate a different character, a character's feelings, or the sounds or atmosphere of the scene and events. They could also consider how loudly or quietly and how fast to read.

A Lesson for Every Day
Literacy
7-8 Years
© A&C Black

Abraham and Sarah

The story of **Abraham and Sarah** is in the book of **Genesis** in the **Old Testament of the Bible**.

- **Read what God said to Abraham.**

Work with a partner.

Abraham and his wife Sarah lived in a city called Haran. They had no children.

One day, when Abraham was seventy-five years old, God said to him, "Leave your country, your people and your father's household and go to a place which I am going to show you. You will be the father of a great nation, and I shall bless you and make your name so great that it will be used in blessings."

- **Make notes about how you could act the parts of Abraham and Sarah.**
  How might they feel about leaving their home?

How can you show this using your face and body?

Abraham	Sarah

- **Act the dialogue.**

NOW TRY THIS!

- **Read the next part of the story.**
- **Act it with a partner.**

Genesis chapter 12

Teachers' note Ask the children how Abraham might have felt about leaving his home and going off to a strange place. Give the children time to think about how he would broach the subject with Sarah. How might she respond? How would she feel about leaving her family and friends?

A Lesson for Every Day
Literacy
7-8 Years
© A&C Black

Adventure peak

- In the flags write headings for the **main events** of a story.

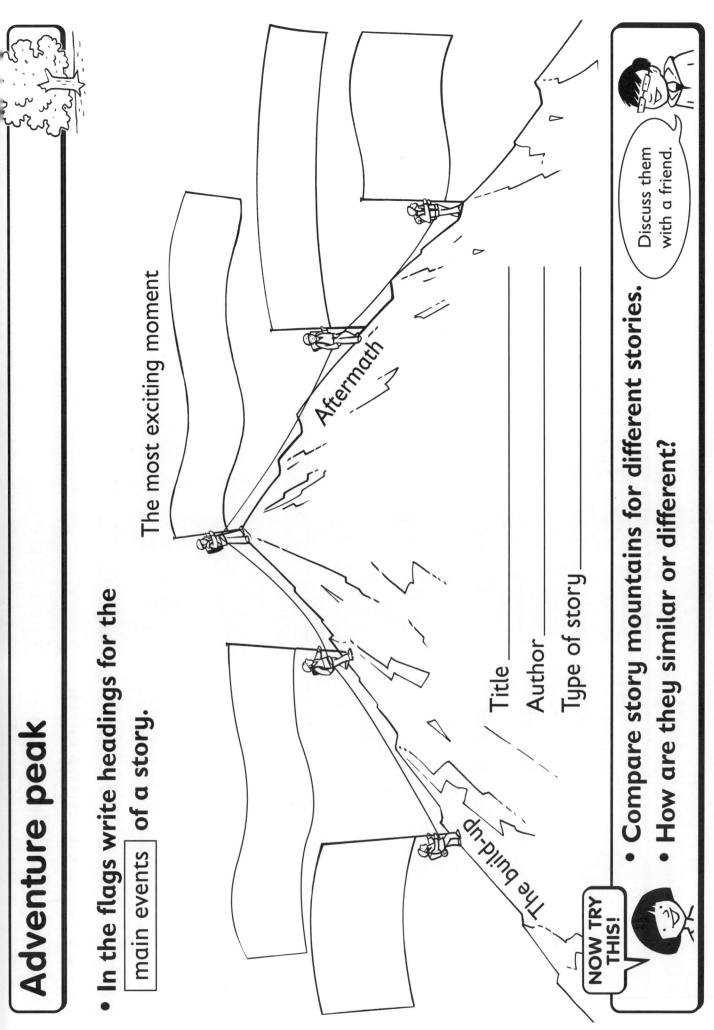

The most exciting moment

Aftermath

The build-up

Title _____

Author _____

Type of story _____

Discuss them with a friend.

NOW TRY THIS!

- Compare story mountains for different stories.
- How are they similar or different?

Teachers' note Use this with an adventure or mystery story. Identify the most exciting part of the story and then trace the main events that lead up to it. Discuss why the events after this are important: for example, to fill in gaps in the story, tie up 'loose ends' and to make links between all the events, especially where details have been kept secret from the reader.

A Lesson for Every Day
Literacy
7–8 Years
© A&C Black

The search

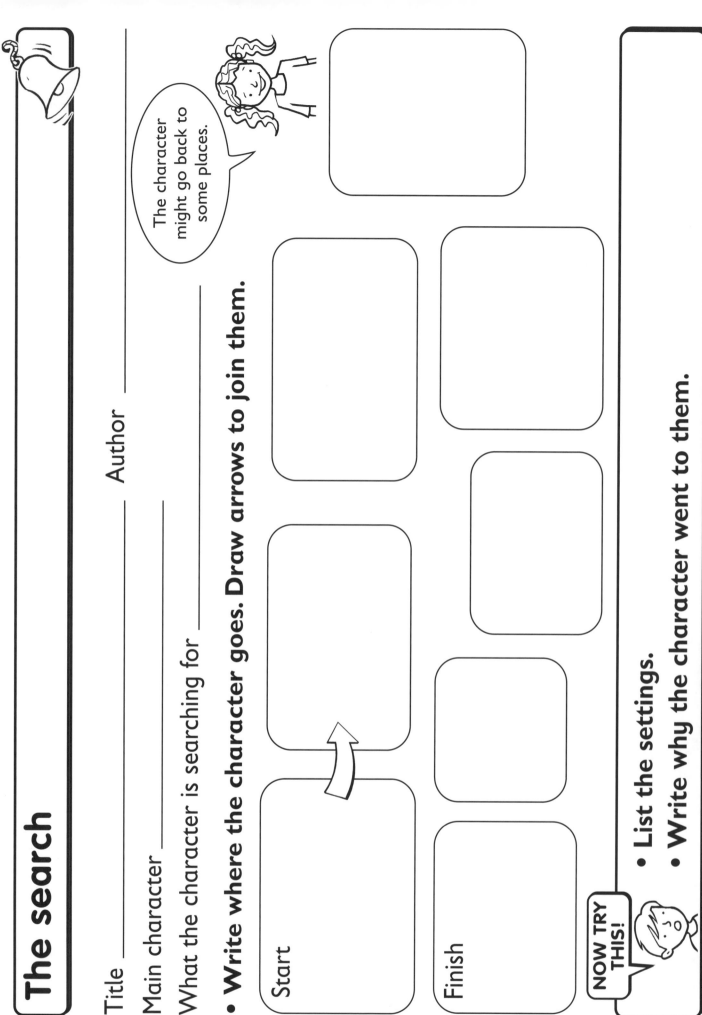

Title _____

Author _____

Main character _____

What the character is searching for _____

The character might go back to some places.

• **Write where the character goes. Draw arrows to join them.**

Start

Finish

NOW TRY THIS!

• List the settings.
• Write why the character went to them.

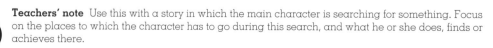

66

Teachers' note Use this with a story in which the main character is searching for something. Focus on the places to which the character has to go during this search, and what he or she does, finds or achieves there.

A Lesson for Every Day
Literacy
7-8 Years
© A&C Black

Wrong to right

What is the main character trying to put right?
- **Draw the character.**
- **Write in the speech bubbles.**

Title _____

Author _____

It is wrong that _____
_____
_____
_____
_____

I shall try to _____
_____
_____
_____
_____

These will make it difficult.
_____
_____
_____
_____

These will help.
_____
_____
_____

Main character
_____

NOW TRY THIS!
- **How does the character try to put things right?**
- **Tell a friend.**

Teachers' note This activity supports the reading of a story in which a character has been the victim of a wrong; the main character sets out to put this right. Tension builds up as he or she has to overcome dangers or difficulties.

A Lesson for Every Day
Literacy
7-8 Years
© A&C Black

In the hot seat

Title _____ Author _____

The answers

Character _____

My questions

Why did you _____

Why did you _____

- What might the character do after the end of the story?
- Write your ideas.

Teachers' note Use this with any story, particularly an adventure or mystery story. While reading it as a serial, different children could take the 'hot seat'. Encourage children to vary the question format, and use 'How will you…?' or 'What will you…?' in order to avoid asking 'why' questions that drift away from the progress of the narrative.

A Lesson for Every Day
Literacy
7–8 Years
© A&C Black

Clues

Title _____

Author _____

The mystery

Who?

What?

Where?

The end
The hidden fact

Clues in the story

NOW TRY THIS!

- **Which was the most important clue?**
- **Write why it was important.**

Teachers' note This could be completed in stages as a shared story is read. You could copy it onto an interactive whiteboard and invite the class to contribute at appropriate stages. How soon can they identify the mystery? What do the clues that they find along the way suggest? Are there any 'red herrings'? What was kept hidden from the reader until near the end?

A Lesson for Every Day
Literacy
7–8 Years
© A&C Black

The Castle Site discovery

There was nothing left of the old castle except the dungeons.

- **What did Persana find out about it in the library?**
- **Write about her discoveries.**

What caught her eye on the contents page?

It lets air out of the dungeons.

Persana laid the old leather-bound book on the wedge of foam as the librarian had shown her. She opened it and skimmed the contents page: Sir Edward Sefton... The building of the castle... Then something caught her eye.

_____

_____

What did Persana find out?

_____

_____

What did she think and figure out?

_____

_____

What question did she ask?

_____

_____

NOW TRY THIS!

- **Does the story sound exciting?**
- **Make some sentences long and some short.**
- **Use** speech marks **for Persana's thoughts.**

Teachers' note Use this to develop a story entitled _The Castle Site_ (see the story starter cards on page 72). The other story starters could be developed in a similar way but with a scene starter supplied by the children. They could read it to a friend, who could ask questions to help them to develop their stories. Point out that a good mystery story should answer the questions that it makes a reader ask.

A Lesson for Every Day
Literacy
7-8 Years
© A&C Black

Mystery story starter cards

Footprints
A trail of footprints appeared in the muddy verge along the lane. They began at the roundabout by the school and stopped where the lane joined the main road. Each footprint was a metre long and the strides measured three metres. They looked as if they had been made by a human or another creature that walked on two legs and had five toes.

The Always Silk Scarf
No one had seen Neil's grandfather without the dark blue silk scarf – night or day. Just before he died he sent for Neil. He tied the scarf carefully around the boy's neck. As he did this his old fingers straightened out and became graceful and supple. His eyes glowed strong and deep. He said, "You, Neil, have been chosen."

The Lake
It was dawn on Midsummer's Day. The inky-black water of Lake Vast began to bubble. The bubbling became stronger and stronger. People talked about the lake ferries that had stopped ten years ago, after the fifth sinking. It happened every ten years, on Midsummer's Day. Neither the boats nor anyone on them was ever found.

The Castle Site
All that could be seen on the site of Sefton Castle was a wide pipe, like a periscope but as wide as a drainpipe, poking up through a flowerbed. Persana asked her mother what it was for. "That's been there for years. It lets air out of the dungeons." In the library Persana found some old maps and papers and learned some strange facts about the castle.

The Bike
The old bike had lain in the shed for as long as anyone could remember. It was rusty, with burst tyres and a broken bell. One morning Grant heard the bell ringing. He went to the shed, but there was the bike, among the tools and plant pots, just as it had always been – or was it? The rust had gone, the tyres were no longer flat and the bell gleamed.

The Midnight Skaters
The pond had frozen over but there was a big sign next to it: DANGER – THIN ICE. One night Emma heard laughter and voices chatting. She looked out of the window. Dozens of people were skating on the pond. There was something unusual about them. Emma realised that they were dressed as if they lived a hundred or so years ago.

The Tapping
One night James heard a tapping sound. It seemed to come from somewhere above the ceiling. The next night he heard it again, and the next, and the next … It began at exactly 10.32pm, with three quick taps, followed by six slow ones. After that the pattern changed – a different pattern each night. It always stopped at 11.59 – a minute before midnight.

The Well
Well House had been named after the old well that had been covered many years before. The council had tried to fill in the well but it seemed to be bottomless, so they plugged it with a big rock. No one could remember exactly where it was. Then one day the people in Well House heard voices under the floor in their living room.

Children from Nowhere
A new boy and a new girl came to school. They looked like twins. The same happened in every class. Not only that – all the boys looked the same and all the girls looked the same. Just their sizes were different. What's more, the girls were all named Nuala and the boys were all named Numo. They all had the same family name – Nufolk.

The Thought Stone
Peter picked up the lovely pink and gold stone he had found on the beach. Then he heard his brother Dan speaking but his voice sounded thin and echoing. His real voice was also saying, "Hurry up, or we'll be late for school." Peter realised that the thin voice was Dan's *thoughts*.

The Magpie's Nest
When Meera found a bird's nest filled with jewellery, coins and all kinds of bits and pieces she thought it must belong to a magpie. She went to look at the nest each day. One day there was a big jewel box in it. A magpie couldn't possibly lift it. How could it have got there?

A Crack in the Street
There was a crowd in the street one morning. People had come out to look at the enormous crack that had appeared down the centre of the street. It was as wide as a car and so deep that no one could see the bottom. There had been no sound. The road had just opened up.

Teachers' note These could be used with the whole class or a group, or the children could work from them individually to start a story, which they can develop by making notes about what happens next and how a character solves the mystery. The pages that follow can be used to help them to develop their stories.

A Lesson for Every Day
Literacy
7–8 Years
© A&C Black

71

- **Imagine what might happen in the story *The Thought Stone*.**
- **Write Peter's answers.**

Make up the story.

What was Dan thinking when you first heard him?

Who else's thoughts did you hear?

What surprises did you have when you heard people's thoughts?

How did hearing people's thoughts change your life?

Peter

NOW TRY THIS!

- **Write three more questions to help you to tell the story.**
- **Write the answers.**

Teachers' note Use this to develop a story entitled *The Thought Stone* (see the story starter cards on 'Mystery story starter cards'). The other story starters could be developed in a similar way but with different questions. The children could work in pairs or individually.

A Lesson for Every Day
Literacy
7–8 Years
© A&C Black

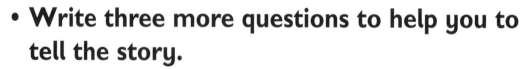

The Always Silk Scarf story mountain

- Write notes to help you to tell the story The Always Silk Scarf.

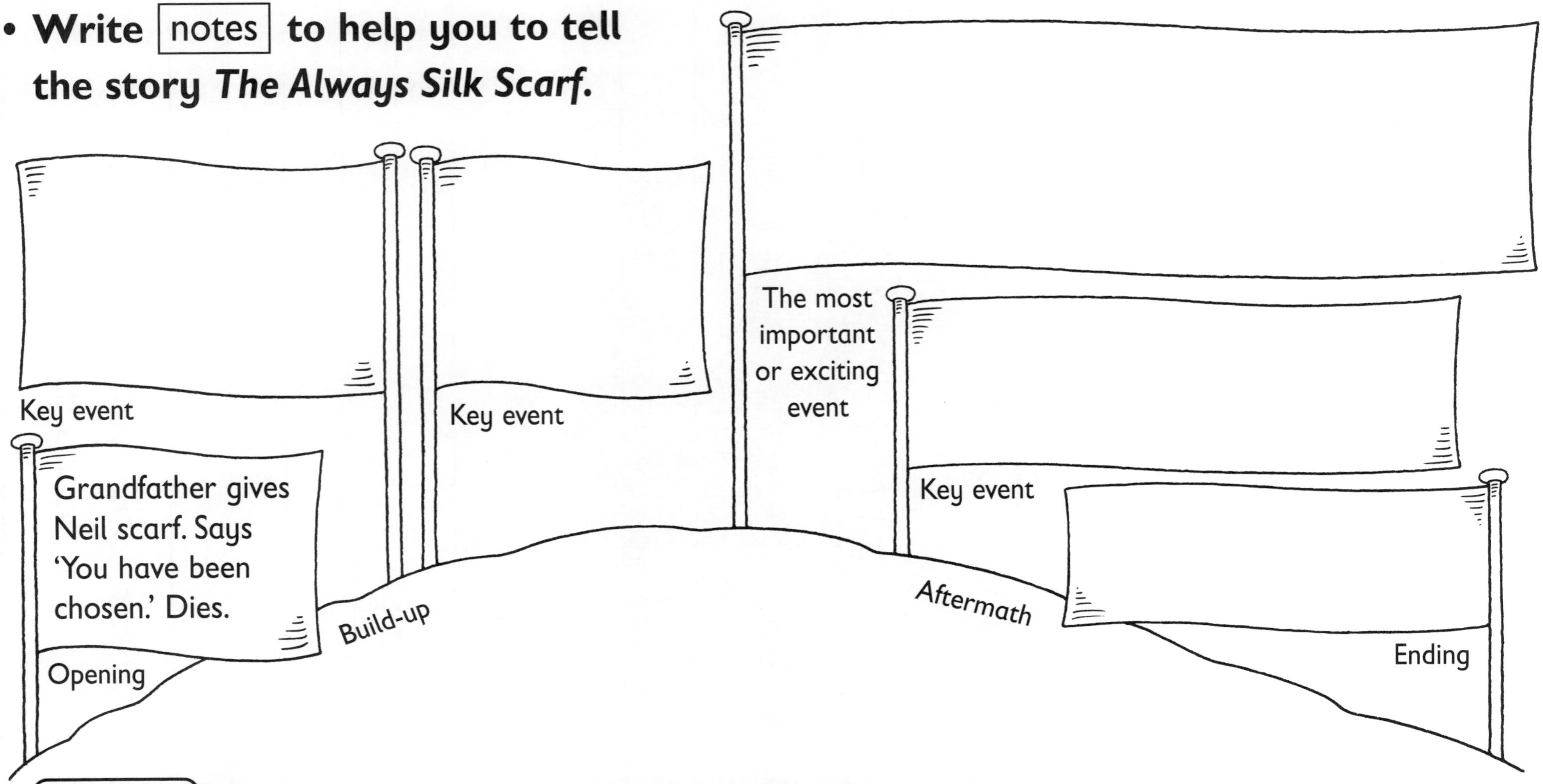

Opening

Grandfather gives Neil scarf. Says 'You have been chosen.' Dies.

Build-up

Key event

Key event

The most important or exciting event

Key event

Aftermath

Ending

NOW TRY THIS!

- Tell the story with a friend.

Teachers' note Use this to develop a story entitled *The Always Silk Scarf* (see the story starter cards on 'Mystery story starter cards'). You could mask and alter the opening to use this with one of the other story starters. The children could work individually, in pairs or in small groups.

A Lesson for Every Day
Literacy
7-8 Years
© A&C Black

A Crack in the Street dialogue

- **What did the people say?**
- **Write in the** speech bubbles **.**
- **Then write this using** speech marks **.**

Make it exciting.

Give the people names.

Look! There's something down there!

"Look! There's something down there!" gasped Adam.

NOW TRY THIS!

- **Act the scene with your group.**
- **Carry on acting the story.**

Teachers' note Use this to develop a story entitled *A Crack in the Street* (see the story starter cards on 'Mystery story starter cards'). The other story starters could be developed in a similar way but with pictures drawn by the children. They could enact and develop the scene in the picture and then write the dialogue in sentences.

A Lesson for Every Day
Literacy
7-8 Years
© A&C Black

Into the past

The **Ancient Greek** myths are from the past.
The passage is written in the present.

- **Change it to the past.**
- **Circle the words you will change.**
- **Rewrite the passage.**

In the land of Colchis there is a fleece from a golden ram. A dragon that never sleeps guards it.

Jason says he will go and get the golden fleece. He has an enormous ship built, and names it *Argo*.

Finally the ship is ready and Jason sets off with his crew, the Argonauts. As soon as they land in Colchis, Jason sends a message to the King. He says that he has come for the golden fleece. The King says he can take it if he can complete two tasks: yoke two fire-breathing bulls to a plough and kill a dragon, then plant its teeth in the ground.

_____

_____

_____

_____

_____

_____

_____

NOW TRY THIS!

- **What do you think happened next?**
- **Write three sentences in the past tense.**

Teachers' note Discuss stories that children know, then ask them if these are written in the present or the past tense and how they can tell. Invite volunteers to give example verbs. Read the passage with them. How can we tell that it is in the present tense? How could it be changed to the past tense? What is the first word you need to change and what would you change it to?

A Lesson for Every Day
Literacy
7–8 Years
© A&C Black

Time travel

The robots can only speak in the [past] tense.

- Change their words to the [present].
- Underline the words to change.
- Write what the robots should say.

The sun was shining all day. The heat was melting my feet.

_____
_____
_____
_____

I was dancing. I liked doing the foxtrot but foxes didn't trot.

_____
_____
_____
_____

I was writing a letter. That was funny. The letter had a lot of letters in it!

_____
_____
_____
_____

NOW TRY THIS!

- **What do you think this robot is saying?**
- **Write in the past then in the present tense.**

Past

Present

Teachers' note Revise the different forms of the past and present tenses of verbs (including the use of auxiliary verbs like _am, is, are, was_ and _were_). Read the first example with them, ask them to identify two different types of past tense (_was shining_ and _melted_) and discuss which forms of the present tense to use (_is shining_ sounds right but _melts_ does not – _is melting_ would be better).

A Lesson for Every Day
Literacy
7–8 Years
© A&C Black

Action sentences

Think about how each character or object might move.
- **Choose a** `doing` **word and a** `place`.
- **Write the sentences.**
- **Read the sentences.**

Doing words

trundled
tumbled
ambled
dabbled
marched
slithered

Places

across the field.
through the grass.
at the edge of the pond.
down the hillside.
along the High Street.
through the village.

The stream _____.

A herd of cattle _____.

The green snake _____.

A dozen soldiers _____.

The huge lorry _____.

Four ducks _____.

NOW TRY THIS!

- **Write a sentence about something else in action.**

Use interesting words.

Teachers' note Remind the children of their previous work on interesting verbs to use instead of was and goes when describing settings. Point out that interesting verbs can help to create a character in a story. Tell them that this page is about the ways in which characters move and that they are looking for interesting verbs to use instead of went.

A Lesson for Every Day
Literacy
7–8 Years
© A&C Black

Exclamation words

This is an exclamation mark ! . It can show all these:

something funny

being pleased

Great goal!

something loud

BANG!

a surprise or fright

Eek!   Aaaagh!   Oh!

• **Write what they are saying. Put in exclamation marks.**

Which snakes are good at maths?

NOW TRY THIS!

• **Write a sentence about a surprise you had.**
• **Write what you said.**

Don't forget the exclamation mark.

Teachers' note Show the children examples of sentences in books which end with exclamation marks. Discuss why there is an exclamation mark. Draw out that it is used at the end of a sentence showing shock, surprise, something funny, something frightening or that someone is pleased and surprised about something. It can follow a single word or exclamation: *Eek! Ouch! Wow! Hurray!*

A Lesson for Every Day
Literacy
7-8 Years
© **A&C Black**

Ha, ha!

- **Match the** `questions` **to the** `answers` .
- **Put in the** `question marks` `?`
  and `exclamation marks` `!` .

What keeps a football stadium cool

Get a pencil

Two biscuits crossed the road. One got run over. What did the other one say

The fans

What should you do if your dog swallows a pen

Frostbite

What do you get if you cross a vampire with an iceberg

A jumbo jet

What do you call an elephant that flies

Crumbs

NOW TRY THIS!

- **Write another 'question and joke answer'.**

Remember the question mark and exclamation mark.

Teachers' note Revise question marks and exclamation marks. What is missing from the end of the sentence in first speech bubble? Then look at the answer to the question and ask what is missing from the end of it. Discuss why an exclamation mark should be used, rather than a full stop. Draw out that this is because it says something funny.

A Lesson for Every Day
Literacy
7–8 Years
© A&C Black

End points

- **Read what the people say.**
- **Put in the full stop** `.` **question mark** `?` **or exclamation mark** `!` .

Help

First, rub the fat into the flour

May I help you

Eek   A dragon

What time is it, please

It's half past four

Sit

NEWS 24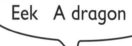

Two men were arrested after last night's burglary

 **NOW TRY THIS!**

- **Put in the missing punctuation marks.**

Come quickly My house is on fire Hello Can you hear me My name is Jack Quick Yes, that's right What did you say My address is 3 Rush Street. What

Teachers' note Remind the children of their earlier work on punctuation at the ends of sentences (Years R, 1 and 2) and discuss the types of sentences which end with full stops or question marks. Ask them to give a sentence or exclamation which would be followed with an exclamation mark and discuss its purpose (to show surprise, shock, fear, anger or that something is funny).

A Lesson for Every Day
Literacy
7–8 Years
© A&C Black

Knock, knock

- Use the joke-bank to write 'knock, knock' jokes in the speech bubbles.

Joke-bank

Darrel

Darrel be the day.

Getta

Getta bell on this door.

Henrietta

Henrietta bag of crisps.

Knock, knock!

Who's there?

Knock, knock!

Who's there?

NOW TRY
THIS!

- Tell another 'knock, knock' joke to a friend.
- Write the joke, using speech bubbles.

Teachers' note The children could collect 'Knock, knock' jokes as a homework activity. Discuss the format of these: how they all start, what the other person says, the reply and the response to this (the punch line). Explain that the words each person says go in a separate speech bubble. The children can then use the joke-bank to help them to complete the jokes.

A Lesson for Every Day
Literacy
7-8 Years
© A&C Black

Story talk

- **Read the passage.**
  What does each character say?

Plop, the little Barn Owl – blue
Mr Barn Owl, his father – red
Mrs Barn Owl, his mother – green

- **Underline only <u>the words they say</u>.**

When the very last firework had faded away, Mr Barn Owl turned to Plop.

'Well, son,' he said. 'I'm off hunting now. Would you like to come?'

Plop looked at the darkness all round them. It seemed even blacker after the bright fireworks. 'Er – not this time, thank you, Daddy. I can't see. I've got stars in my eyes.'

'I see,' said his father. 'In that case I shall have to go by myself.' He floated off into the darkness like a giant white moth.

Plop turned in distress to his mother.

'I *wanted* to go with him. I *want* to like the dark. It's just that I don't seem to be able to.'

'You will be able to, Plop. I'm quite sure about that.'

'I'm not sure,' said Plop.

'Well, I *am*,' his mother said. 'Now, come on. You'd better have your rest. You were awake half the day.'

So Plop had his midnight rest, and when he woke up, his father was back with his dinner. Plop swallowed it in one gulp. 'That was nice,' he said. 'What was it?'

'A mouse,' said Mr Barn Owl.

'I like mouse,' said Plop. 'What's next?'

'I have no idea,' his father said. 'It's Mummy's turn now. You'll have to wait till she gets back.'

From *The Owl Who Was Afraid of the Dark* Jill Tomlinson

NOW TRY THIS!

- **What do you think the owls said next?**

Think about how to show the words they said.

- **Write what each owl said.**

Teachers' note Revise speech bubbles. Point out that only the spoken words are in the speech bubbles. Ask them to read the passage and to find the words people say. Ask how the words are marked out from the rest of the sentence. Point out the use of *said* to introduce or end speech and note that the spoken words are surrounded by speech marks.

A Lesson for Every Day
Literacy
7–8 Years
© A&C Black

If animals could talk

• **Read what the characters said.**

1

Uh, oh – humans wearing silly hats. Watch out.

Yes – they might have dogs, too.

2

Something should be done about dogs that chase us.

We could get the cattle to help.

3

We can take a short cut. Sheep won't harm us.

No – but the cattle might.

4

Eeek! A bull!

That will keep them out.

• **Between the speech marks, write what they said.**

The sheep were munching grass, minding their own business, when along came a group of people.

"_____," said a sheep.

"_____," said another sheep, "they_____."

"Something _____," said the first sheep.

"We _____," answered the second sheep.

Someone opened the gate and said, "We can _____

_____."

"_____," muttered the first sheep.

The bull came charging into the field to help.

"_____," yelled the people.

"_____," said the bull.

NOW TRY THIS!

• **Look for a short comic strip.**
• **Write the dialogue, using speech marks.**

Teachers' note Remind the children of the use of speech marks to surround speech and words such as *said* to introduce or follow the spoken words. Ask them what the first sheep says. Draw out that only these words should be written between the speech marks.

A Lesson for Every Day
Literacy
7–8 Years
© A&C Black

Speech marks

Speech marks are used instead of a speech bubble.

Would you like to be my friend? — Nina

Nina said, "Would you like to be my friend?"

"Yes!" said Toby.

Yes. — Toby

• **Write the words between the speech marks.**

What is your favourite book, Raj? — Simon

I like <u>The Sheep Pig</u> by Dick King-Smith. — Raj

That's the book of the film <u>Babe</u>. — Emily

"What's _____," asked Simon.

"_____,"

said Raj.

"_____," said Emily.

NOW TRY THIS!

• **What could Simon ask Raj about the book?**
• **What might Raj answer?**
• **Write what they say.**

Use speech marks.

_____

_____

84

Teachers' note Remind children of the purpose of speech marks and ask them to look at the other punctuation marks in the sentences. Draw out that they always come just before a speech mark and explain how commas, question marks or exclamation marks are used to end the spoken part when the sentence continues with *said* or another word for *said*.

A Lesson for Every Day
Literacy
7–8 Years
© A&C Black

Speech on the page

- **Look carefully at the speech bubbles and the sentences with speech marks.**
- **What differences can you see? Talk to a friend about them.**
- **Circle them in red.**

Mum said she'll take us swimming.

Gemma

Great. I'll go and ask Dad if I can come.

Tara

"Mum said she'll take us swimming," said Gemma.

"Great," said Tara.

"I'll go and ask Dad if I can come."

- **Write what they say.**
- **Use speech marks.**

Bring your bike. There's a safe place to ride them near our house.

Tom

Ok. I'll be there at about 2 o'clock.

Dan

_____

_____

NOW TRY THIS!

- **Write a phone conversation using these.**

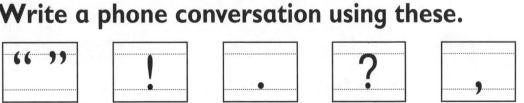

| " " | ! | . | ? | , |

Teachers' note Remind children of the purpose of speech marks and ask them to look at the other punctuation marks in the sentences. Draw out that they always come just before a speech mark and explain how commas, question marks or exclamation marks are used to end the spoken part when the sentence continues with *said* or another word for *said*.

A Lesson for Every Day
Literacy
7-8 Years
© A&C Black

Sale

- **The Green family wants to buy a new puppy.**
- **Mr Green thinks they should sell some things to raise the money.**
- **Which three things should they sell?**
- **Which three things should they keep?**

Work with a group.

Mrs Green's bike

Charlie's remote-controlled car

Mark's violin

Mr Green's breadmaker

Ellie's train set

Widescreen TV

Sell		Keep	
Object	**Reason**	**Object**	**Reason**

NOW TRY THIS!

- **Choose the most important thing to keep.**
- **Explain why.**

Talk to someone from another group.

Teachers' note Ask the children to discuss the family's possessions and to choose three to sell and three to keep. The group should agree on what to write in the chart. They could make a note of their own views and their reasons first and explain these to the others. Point out that it can sometimes be good to change our minds when we listen to someone else's views.

A Lesson for Every Day
Literacy
7–8 Years
© A&C Black

Pairs

The Sun is low
in the sky.

The Sun is high
in the sky.

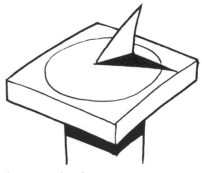

A sundial.

The mug blocks light
coming from the lamp.

The Sun looks as if it
moves across the sky.

Transparent materials.

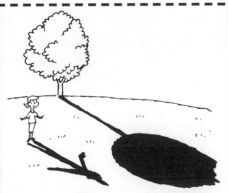

The shadows are long.

The shadows are short.

2 o'clock

Tell the time.

A shadow is formed.

Shadows
change direction.

Light passes
through some things.

Teachers' note Give the page to a group to cut out the two sets and pair the cards. They could take turns to match two pictures and explain how they are linked. The others can question and discuss the pairing: the group should agree on each pairing. They could then glue the pictures onto a sheet of paper, link each pair with arrows and write a sentence on each arrow to show how the ideas are linked.

A Lesson for Every Day
Literacy
7–8 Years
© A&C Black

Discussion words

- **Sort the cards into sets.**
- **Decide with your group how to do this.**

That's a good idea.	That's stupid.	Hmmmm.
What do you think?	Tell us about your idea.	What else?
Just be quiet!	We're not doing that.	What about Sam's idea?
We could try this …	What if …?	Oh.
What for?	No way. Don't even think of it.	I'm not sure about that.

NOW TRY THIS!

- **Tell another group how you sorted the cards.**

A Lesson for Every Day
Literacy
7-8 Years
© A&C Black

What if...?

- Work in a group.
- Read part of a fiction book together.
- **What choices do the characters make?**
- **What could they have done instead?**

Word bank

because	could	if	in case	maybe
	might	possibly	should	so
	then	whether	why	would

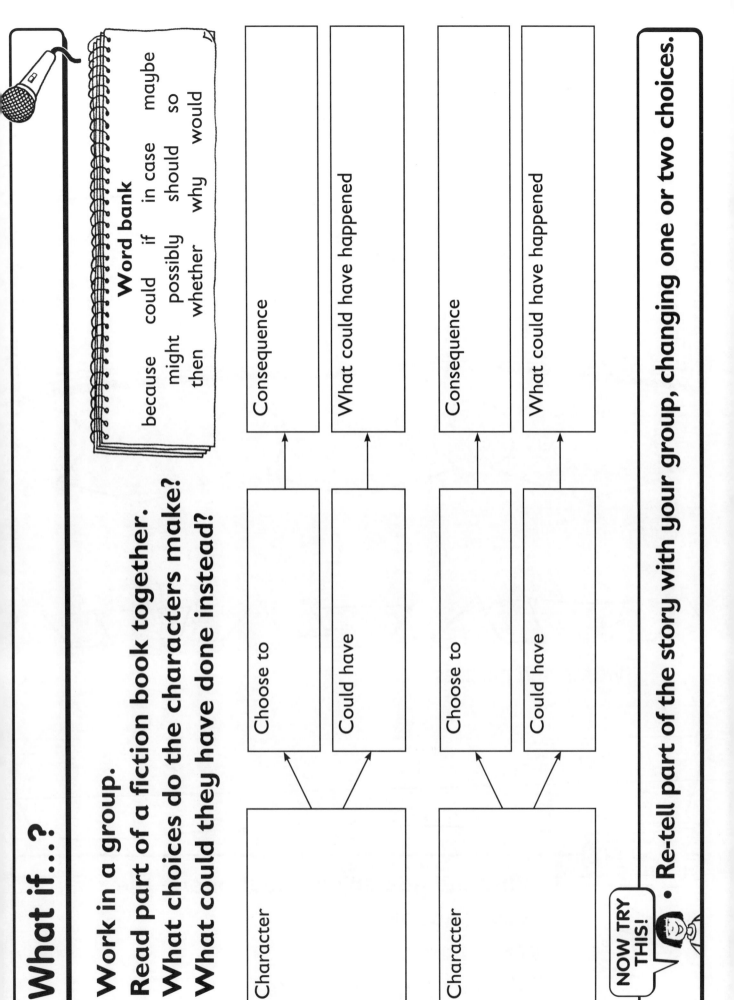

Character

→ **Choose to** → **Consequence**

→ **Could have** → **What could have happened**

Character

→ **Choose to** → **Consequence**

→ **Could have** → **What could have happened**

NOW TRY THIS!

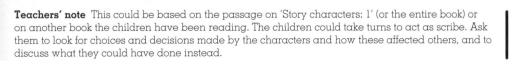

- Re-tell part of the story with your group, changing one or two choices.

A Lesson for Every Day
Literacy
7-8 Years
© A&C Black

Teachers' note This could be based on the passage on 'Story characters: 1' (or the entire book) or on another book the children have been reading. The children could take turns to act as scribe. Ask them to look for choices and decisions made by the characters and how these affected others, and to discuss what they could have done instead.

An author I like

Author _____

My favourite...

... books

... characters

... words and phrases

NOW TRY THIS!

- **What did you enjoy about one of the author's books?**
- **Write notes.**
- **Tell your group about it.**

Teachers' note The children could choose an author whose work they like and use this page to help them to prepare a short presentation to the class. Ask the others if the presentation makes them want to read this author's books, and why.

A Lesson for Every Day
Literacy
7-8 Years
© A&C Black

Notes for a letter

- **Plan a** `letter` **to an** `author` .
- **Write notes on the notepads.**

Author's name _____

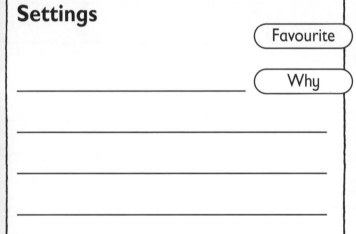

Author's books you have read or seen on TV or film

_____

_____

_____

_____

(Favourite)

(Why)

(Questions)

Characters

_____

_____

_____

_____

Settings

_____

_____

_____

_____

(Favourite)

(Why)

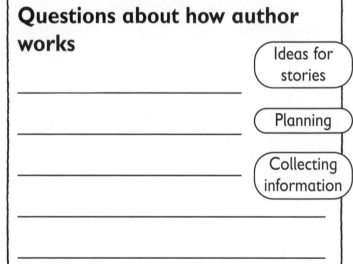

Questions about how author works

_____

_____

_____

(Ideas for stories)

(Planning)

(Collecting information)

NOW TRY THIS!

- **Use your notes to help you to write three sentences for your letter.**

Teachers' note The children first need to have read different kinds of letters and to know that people write letters for many different purposes: for example, to thank, congratulate, give news, ask for information, complain or discuss something. Before they plan a letter to an author they need to be clear why they are writing: for example, to find out where ideas for stories come from.

A Lesson for Every Day
Literacy
7–8 Years
© A&C Black

Notes to sentences

• **Turn the notes into** sentences **for a** letter **to an author.**

Read most of author's books	<u>I have read most of your books.</u>
Favourite – *The Sheep-Pig*	_____ _____
Saw film of it – *Babe* but book better	_____ _____
V. sad when dog's puppies taken away	_____ _____
Knows a lot about sheep + sheepdogs. How?	_____ _____
What gave idea for story?	_____ _____

NOW TRY THIS!

• **Plan a letter to an author whose books you like.**

Check first. Is the author still alive?

Teachers' note Use this to develop the letters planned on 'Notes for a letter'. Point out the difference between notes and finished writing: notes are jotted quickly to record ideas and need not be full sentences. They can be developed into different kinds of sentence written in different ways, depending on the purpose: for example, to state a fact, ask a question, make a suggestion, persuade or explain.

A Lesson for Every Day
Literacy
7–8 Years
© A&C Black

A letter to an author

- **Write a** [letter] **to an author.**

Make notes first.

Your address _____

_____

_____

Postcode _____

Date _____

Dear _____

You do not know the author, so write his or her full name.

_____

_____

Books you like. Also film or TV versions.

_____

_____

Characters

_____

_____

Settings

_____

_____

Questions about how the author works.

_____

Finishing sentence

_____

Signing-off

_____

Your name

Teachers' note Use this to develop the children's letters planned on 'Notes for a letter' and 'Notes to sentences'. Point out the main features of the layout of a letter and introduce terms such as 'greeting' and 'signing-off'. Remind the children that they are writing to someone they do not know well and give examples of the type of language to use (see the notes on the activity on page 12).

A Lesson for Every Day
Literacy
7-8 Years
© A&C Black

Read this book

- **Write a** `letter` **to someone you know to tell him or her about a book you enjoyed.**

Dear _____

_____

Name the book and the author.

Say where it is set.

Say who it is about and what the character is like.

Tell your friend about the story but don't give away the ending.

Say what you liked about it.

Write a finishing sentence.

Sign off.

Teachers' note Remind the children of what they know about setting out a letter (see 'A letter to an author') and point out that this is a letter to someone they know well. Ask them how this will make it different from a letter to an author.

A Lesson for Every Day
Literacy
7–8 Years
© A&C Black

Setting sentences

- **Make sentences to describe settings**
- **Match each building to a** `doing` **word and a place.**
- **Write the sentences.**
- **Read the sentences.**

On the chart, colour the words you use. Use a different colour for each sentence.

Building	What the building did	Place
Valley Farm	guarded	along the old railway.
High House	squatted among	the town.
Elm Street School	clung to	on a hilltop overlooking the village.
Station Cottages	nestled in	the wall of the church.
Priory Mews	perched on	in a hollow by a stream.
Rook Castle	stretched along	among gas works and old warehouses.

_____

_____

_____

_____

_____

NOW TRY THIS!

- **Write a sentence about the setting of a building you know.**

Use interesting words.

Teachers' note Begin with three sentences about locations: for example, *The road goes through the village, The river goes through the gorge, Huge trucks go along the High Street.* Discuss other verbs to use instead of *goes: The road snakes through the village, The river rushes through the gorge, Huge trucks trundle along the High Street.*

A Lesson for Every Day
Literacy
7-8 Years
© A&C Black

All change

- **Change the** adjectives **to match the pictures.**

Jack is a smart young man.

These rough square stones were on the beach.

The sea was calm and smooth.

He wore a fresh clean t-shirt.

I drew a long straight line.

We found a large empty box.

NOW TRY THIS!

- **Write four adjectives to describe these.**

    a house   a car   a street

Change the adjectives to make the descriptions different.

Teachers' note Remind the children of their previous learning about words that describe and introduce the term *adjective* if you have not done so already. The children are required to identify the two *adjectives* in each caption and to change them for others which better describe the picture.

A Lesson for Every Day
Literacy
7–8 Years
© **A&C Black**

Verb detective

Help the verb detective.

walk
run
skip

• **Circle the verbs.**

The goddess Persephone lived in Ancient Greece. Her mother was the goddess Demeter, who made all the plants grow everywhere on Earth. In those days there was no winter or autumn. It was always spring or summer.

One day, when Persephone was playing in the fields, the ground opened. A deafening sound rumbled from the hole and a chariot came roaring out. Dark horses pulled it. Hades, the god of the Underworld was riding the chariot.

Hades grabbed Persephone and took her to the Underworld to be his wife. The hole closed behind them.

Demeter looked all over the Earth for Persephone. She became so sad that she forgot all about the plants, so they did not grow. The first winter arrived.

Then a shepherd found Persephone's belt. He took it to Demeter.

"Where did you find it?" asked Demeter. The shepherd showed her. Demeter guessed what had happened. She told Zeus, the King of the Gods, "If you don't tell Hades to let Persephone go, I will stop making the plants grow. The Earth shall have nothing but winter."

Zeus ordered Hades to free Persephone. Demeter went to meet her, but Persephone could not leave the Underworld. She had eaten some pomegranate seeds. There was an old law about this. Anyone who had eaten in the Underworld had to stay there.

Demeter thought hard. A plan formed in her mind.

NOW TRY THIS!

• **What do you think Demeter did?**
• **Write three sentences about it.**
• **Circle the verbs.**

Teachers' note Remind the children of the different purposes of words in a sentence: to name people or things (or to use instead of these names), to show actions, to say where, when or why things happened and to show belonging. Tell them that they are going to investigate words for actions and introduce the term *verb* for these words.

A Lesson for Every Day
Literacy
7–8 Years
© A&C Black

Verb sort

- **Cut out the cards.**
  Sort them into two sets: ⏐ nouns ⏐ **and** ⏐ verbs ⏐ .

 Nouns are words for people, animals, places and things.

Verbs are words for actions.

- **Take turns to pick up a card from each set.**
- **Use them to complete this sentence.**

  The girls _____ the _____ .

- **Write the sentences.**

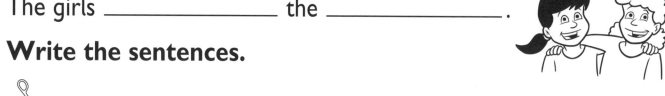

boat	cactus	car	catch
chase	climb	daisy	eggs
elephant	feed	follow	hide
hug	jelly	lamp post	mend
moon	mountain	paperclip	ride
sausages	scrub	sky	slap
snowflake	throw	tickle	weigh

Teachers' note It is useful to glue each set of words onto a different coloured card to facilitate keeping them in two sets: nouns and verbs. Remind the children of their previous learning about the purposes of words in sentences, particularly nouns and verbs, before they play the game. Note that sentences can make sense as sentences even if they say something silly.

A Lesson for Every Day
Literacy
7-8 Years
© A&C Black

Food guards

KITCHEN

Stop! Only 'good-for-you' foods are allowed.

- **Choose a 'good-for-you' food from the list. Find out as much as you can about it.**
- **Plan a talk to tell the food guards why it should be allowed in the kitchen.**

Notes for my talk

Food _____

Why I chose it

- _____
- _____
- _____
- _____
- _____
- _____

Foods
avocado
banana
bread
cheese
chips
chocolate
ice cream
jam
milk
orange
peanut butter
sprouts
toffee

- **Explain why you chose this food. Your group should vote** `yes` **or** `no` **on whether to let it into the kitchen.**

Work in a group.

NOW TRY THIS!

- **Together, choose a food which should not be let in. Write five reasons to explain why.**

Teachers' note The children will need access to information books, leaflets and websites about food and nutrition. Ask them, working individually, to make notes on the chart about why the food guards should allow their chosen food into the kitchen: for example, it is tasty, nutritious (in what way?), cheap and so on. The children then take turns to explain to the rest of the group, who act as 'food guards'.

A Lesson for Every Day
Literacy
7–8 Years
© A&C Black

Sandwich

- **Talk about the best way to pack a sandwich.**
- **What must the package do?**

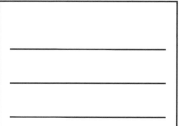
Work with a group.

Keep it clean.			

- **Draw your package.**

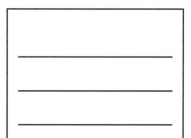
Talk about it then choose someone to draw it and someone to write the labels.

- **Write what you will do and who will do it.**

Action	Who will do it

NOW TRY THIS!

- **Make your sandwich package.**
- **Test it.**

Teachers' note This could support work in design and technology on packaging. The children could make sketches and notes of their ideas before sharing them with their group. Remind them about words to use in polite discussion and that everyone's views should be considered.

A Lesson for Every Day
Literacy
7-8 Years
© A&C Black

Guess who

• Work in a large group.

☆ Get into pairs. Each pair will need a card.

☆ Plan a conversation between the characters on your card.

☆ The others in your group have to guess who you are.

How will you change your voice?

Talk to your partner about this.

snowman and snow woman

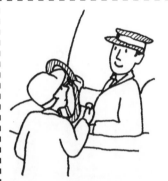

bus driver and passenger

traffic warden and driver

police officer and burglar

sheep and sheepdog

Father Christmas and toyshop manager

magician and rabbit

chef and waiter

butterfly and caterpillar

Teachers' note Cut out the cards and give one to each pair of children. You could make the activity easier by letting the children see all the cards and cut them out for themselves. Allow time for discussion and planning in pairs, then ask the children to take turns to enact the dialogue between the characters on their card. It is useful to model with another adult how to speak in role.

A Lesson for Every Day
Literacy
7–8 Years
© A&C Black

Digging up the past

- **Work in a group of four.**
- **Imagine you are four** | archaeologists | **on a dig.**

☆ Cut out the cards.

☆ Take one each.

☆ Take turns to describe your **artefact** to the group.

> What does it look like? What could it have been used for?

Coins

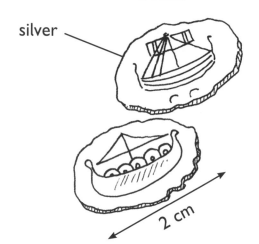

silver

2 cm

Clay pot

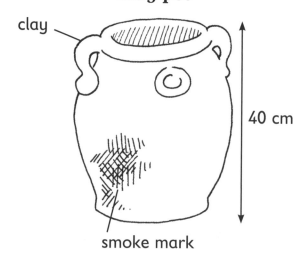

clay

40 cm

smoke mark

Loom weights

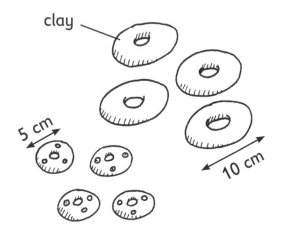

clay

5 cm

10 cm

Stones for grinding flour

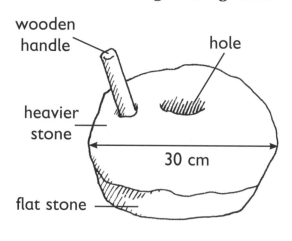

wooden handle

hole

heavier stone

30 cm

flat stone

NOW TRY THIS!

- **Work with a partner.**
- **'Dig up' another artefact. Tell your partner what you can learn from it.**

Teachers' note Link this activity with work in history on invaders and settlers, providing relevant background information. Begin by exploring any terms the children are not familiar with. The children should be encouraged to speak in role as archaeologists. For the extension activity, prepare a mock dig by hiding replica artefacts (or pictures of artefacts) in a tray filled with sand.

A Lesson for Every Day
Literacy
7-8 Years
© A&C Black

Lost in the woods

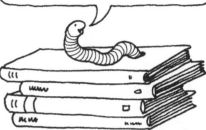

The characters should be from different books.

- **Work in a group of four.**
- **Each choose a character from a book you know well.**
- **Draw your character and make notes about his or her** | personality |

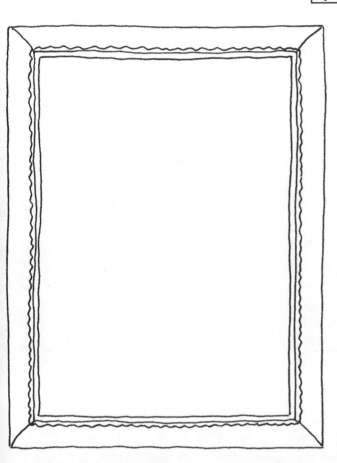

Notes

- **Imagine that these four characters get lost in a forest. What do they do? What do they say? Act the scene with your group.**

How will you keep your audience interested?

NOW TRY THIS!

- **Imagine that two characters find their way out of the forest. Act the scene.**

Work with a partner.

Teachers' note Provide a selection of books from which the children can choose their characters. Ask them to re-read the book (or parts of it) to remind themselves about their characters personality. When enacting the scene, they should think about how the character might respond to being lost in the forest. Link this with work in citizenship on communities and human rights.

A Lesson for Every Day
Literacy
7-8 Years
© A&C Black

In the wrong

Imagine a friend asks you to do something wrong:

Lucy

> I'm not speaking to Ella.
> You're *my* friend.
> Don't talk to her.
> Don't play with her.

Patrick

Ella

What would you say?

- **Work with a partner.**
- **Act the scene.**
- **Write what you both said.**

> What will you say to make your audience interested?

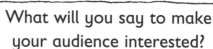

NOW TRY THIS!

- **What other wrong action might someone ask you to do? Act a | dialogue | about it.**

Teachers' note This could develop from work in citizenship lessons on right and wrong. Give the children a few minutes to consider what they might say if they were the friend of Patrick, and why they might not do what they know is right in this situation. Encourage pairs to prepare the dialogue between Patrick and Lucy for an audience. They can take turns to write what they said in the speech bubbles.

A Lesson for Every Day
Literacy
7–8 Years
© A&C Black

Victims

- ## Work with a partner.

- ## Plan how to act the role of <u>one</u> of the victims:
  ### – as their property is stolen

feelings	thoughts

– later

feelings and worries	thoughts

- ## Speak the victim's feelings, worries and thoughts. Speak as if you are the victims.
- ## What is she/he most worried about?

Use 'I' and 'me'.

NOW TRY THIS!
- ## Role-play what happens to the mugger. Does she/he feel guilty? Does she/he get caught?

Teachers' note After the planning stage, introduce and explain the term 'monologue'. Invite volunteers to speak in the role of the victim. Explain that although victims might not speak all their thoughts in real life, a monologue is useful in drama for expressing thoughts and feelings.

A Lesson for Every Day
Literacy
7–8 Years
© A&C Black

Costume drama

- **Choose a film character with an interesting costume.**
- **Draw and label the costume.**

Describe the colours, materials and style.

- **Write a caption.**
  (What is the film? Who is the character? How does the costume show what the character is like?)

_____

_____

_____

_____

_____

NOW TRY THIS!

- **Imagine two characters swapped costumes. Describe how this would affect the audience.**

Teachers' note This could be based on a television programme or film the children have watched as a group or on one they have watched independently. Ask them to think of a costume which told the audience something about the character wearing it: for example, the furs worn by Cruella De Vil in *101 Dalmatians*, or Superman's outfit.

A Lesson for Every Day
Literacy
7–8 Years
© A&C Black

King Midas's wish

- **Read the** main events **of the story.**
- **Answer the questions.**

King Midas found Silenus sleeping in his palace garden. When he woke up, Midas gave him a meal and let him stay in the palace.

Silenus stayed for twelve days. Then Midas took him in his chariot to Mount Olympus, the home of the gods.

The god Bacchus came to meet them. He was so pleased to see his friend Silenus safe that he told Midas he would grant any wish for him.

Midas said, "Let everything I touch turn into gold." The gods all said that this was a foolish wish.

1 What did Midas wish?

He wished that _____

_____

_____

2 Why do you think Midas wished this?

I think Midas _____

_____

_____

3 Did the gods think Midas's wish was a wise one? _____

4 What do you think? _____

_____

_____

_____

5 Why? _____

_____

_____

 **NOW TRY THIS!**

- **Read the story of Midas.**
- **Write two sentences about the next main event.**

Teachers' note This could be used to introduce the story of King Midas. Explain that many myths have a wish as the main event which sets in train the other events of the story. Discuss what might happen as a result of Midas's wish. How could he change his wish to make it less foolish?

A Lesson for Every Day
Literacy
7-8 Years
© A&C Black

Pantomime characters

- **Work in a group.**
- **Plan a** | pantomime | **for younger children on:**
- **Write** | notes | **about the** | characters |.

Cinderella

Character	Notes
 Cinderella	_____ _____ _____ _____
 Ugly Sisters	_____ _____ _____
 Fairy godmother	_____ _____ _____
 Prince	_____ _____ _____

> Man, woman, girl, boy or animal?
> About how old?
> Good or bad?
> What do they look like?
> How are they related to other characters?

NOW TRY THIS!

- **What other characters are sometimes in** *Cinderella* **pantomimes?**
- **Draw them and write notes about them.**

Teachers' note Remind the children of the story of Cinderella by inviting them to take turns to retell it. Ask them to think about what they know about each character, what they did and said and how and why they did and said these things.

108

A Lesson for Every Day
Literacy
7–8 Years
© A&C Black

Pantomime dialogue: 1

- **What are the pantomime** [characters] **saying?**
- **Write in the** [speech bubbles] **.**

NOW TRY THIS!

- **Draw the next three** [scenes] **.**
- **Write what the characters say.**

Teachers' note First see 'pantomime characters'. The children could enact the scenes in the pictures before completing the speech bubbles.

A Lesson for Every Day
Literacy
7–8 Years
© A&C Black

Pantomime dialogue: 2

- **Look at the pictures with the** speech bubbles **you wrote.**
- **Write them as** dialogue **.**

Use speech marks.

" "

"_____

_____ ," said the first Ugly Sister to Cinderella.

"_____

_____ ," said Cinderella.

When the day of the ball came Cinderella had to do the ugly sisters' hair.

"_____ ," said the second Ugly Sister, "_____

_____ ."

"_____ ," said Cinderella.

Then the ugly sisters set off for the ball.

"_____

_____ ," said the first Ugly Sister.

"_____

_____ ," said Cinderella.

Cinderella stayed at home, sewing. Then she heard a voice.

_____

_____

NOW TRY THIS!

- **Write four more sentences of the dialogue.**

Teachers' note First see 'pantomime dialogue 1'. Ask them to reread what they wrote in the speech bubbles and remind them of the conventions of written dialogue using direct speech, particularly the positions of the speech marks and other punctuation marks.

A Lesson for Every Day
Literacy
7-8 Years
© A&C Black

- **Read the** dialogue **you wrote.**
- **Write it as a** play script **.**

Work with a friend.

Characters	Spoken words
Ugly Sister 1	_____ _____
Cinderella	_____ _____
Ugly Sister 2	_____ _____
Cinderella	_____ _____
Ugly Sister 1	_____ _____
Cinderella	_____ _____
Cinderella	_____ _____
Fairy godmother	_____ _____

NOW TRY THIS!

- **What happened next?**
- **Write the next scene.**

Teachers' note The children should first have completed 'Pantomime dialogue 1 and 2'. Ask them to reread the dialogue they wrote using speech bubbles. Ask them how they would change this to make it into a play script. Ensure that they know that neither speech bubbles nor words such as *said* are used in a play script and point out how the layout shows who speaks and what they say.

A Lesson for Every Day
Literacy
7-8 Years
© A&C Black

Television talk

Will Burntull talked to Mikkel on the television news.

Will: Good morning, Mikkel. You're the first wheelbarrow race champion I've met. Tell us about this wheelbarrow.

Mikkel: It began as a normal wheelbarrow – the kind you'd use in the garden.

Will: Well, it's not like <u>my</u> wheelbarrow.

Mikkel: No. We changed the shape to make it streamlined. We made it lighter, too.

Will: The wheel looks different too.

Mikkel: Yes. It's very light, but bigger than on a normal wheelbarrow.

- ## Between the speech marks, write what they said.

"_____

_____,"

said Will Burntull.

"_____

_____," said Mikkel.

"_____," said Will.

"_____

_____," said Mikkel.

"_____," said Will.

"_____," said Mikkel. "It's_____."

NOW TRY THIS!

- ## Write your own short interview with a friend.

112

Teachers' note Ask volunteers to read the parts of Will and Mikkel. Discuss how they know what to say. Point out that play scripts do not have speech bubbles or speech marks; the spoken words follow the speaker's name. You could point out how this is made to stand out from the spoken words (usually in bold or upper case).

A Lesson for Every Day
Literacy
7–8 Years
© A&C Black

Scriptwriter

- ## Read the passage with a friend.
- ## Write it as a playscript.

The Wind said to the Sun, "I am much more powerful than you. Watch how hard I can blow."

"No. I am more powerful than you. Watch how brightly I can shine."

"I don't know what's happening to the weather," said a man down below. "The forecast said it would be calm and cloudy."

The Wind said to the Sun, "I can get that man's coat off him but you can't."

"Yes, I can," said the Sun.

"We'll see," said the Wind, and he blew and blew.

Character	What he or she said
Wind	_____
Sun	_____
Man	_____
Wind	_____
Sun	_____
Wind	_____

NOW TRY THIS!

- ## Write the next two lines of the script.
- ## Rewrite them using speech marks.

Teachers' note Children should first have completed 'Television talk'. Give the chhildren copies of their completed 'Television talk' in addition to a copy of this page and ask them to compare the play script and the dialogue they wrote using speech marks. Ask them what they did to convert this dialogue into a play script.

A Lesson for Every Day
Literacy
7-8 Years
© A&C Black

- **Underline the spoken words in blue.**
- **Read these with your group.**

Each read the words of a different character.

An old miller was dying, so he called for his three sons. "I give the mill to you, my eldest son," he said. Then, "To you, my second son, I give my donkey." Then he turned to his youngest son and said, "You, my youngest son, shall have my cat."

The youngest son grumbled, "It is all very well for my brothers. They can earn a living with the mill and the donkey. How am I to make a living when all I have is a cat?"

The cat heard him and said, "Don't worry, master. You shall not starve. I have a plan."

"*You* have a plan!" cried the young man. "But what can *you* do?"

"Wait and see," replied the cat. "Just give me a sack and a pair of boots."

So, off went the youngest son to get a sack and a pair of boots for the cat.

The cat pulled on the boots and went off with the sack over his shoulder. He put it near a rabbit burrow, filled it with thistles and waited. Before long a rabbit came out and began to nibble the thistles. As soon as it was inside, the cat sprang out and tied a rope round the sack. He set off to the royal palace.

A guard stopped him and said, "Where do you think you're going? This is the royal palace."

"I have a present – a nice fat rabbit – for the King," said the cat.

"I am not sure … I do not think I should … You could have a weapon in that …"

As he spoke the cat slipped past him into the palace and took the rabbit to the King. He bowed low and said, "Your majesty, I have a fine fat rabbit in this sack – a gift for you from my master, the Marquis of Carabas."

"How kind!" said the King, taking the sack. "Please thank your master."

Adapted from *Puss in Boots* by Charles Perrault

NOW TRY THIS!

- **Underline in red the words that say what the characters did.**

Teachers' note Use this with 'Dialogue to script 2'. The children could first read the story aloud in groups, with different children reading the parts of the narrator, the miller, the youngest son, the cat and the king. They can then identify the spoken words. They should not include words such as *said*, which introduce speech.

A Lesson for Every Day
Literacy
7–8 Years
© A&C Black

- **Write a** playscript **for the passage from** *Puss in Boots.*

You do not need speech marks.

List of characters

_____   _____
_____   _____
_____   _____
_____   _____

Character	Spoken words
Miller	
Youngest son	

NOW TRY THIS!

- **Write stage directions for the characters.**

Teachers' note Use this with 'Dialogue to script 1'. After reading the story aloud in a group, the children should be able to identify the characters. They will have underlined the spoken words and so should be able to write them in the appropriate places. Ask them to read the playscript as a group and to say how it is different from the story version.

A Lesson for Every Day
Literacy
7-8 Years
© A&C Black

Growing sentences

- **Read the short sentence.**
- **Add some words to make a long sentence.**
- **Make two different long sentences.**

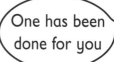
One has been done for you

1 Jack opened the book.

a _Jack opened the story book and began to read._

b _Jack opened the book and looked at the pictures._

2 Mum poured a glass of water.

a _____

_____

b _____

_____

3 The dog rushed towards me.

a _____

_____

b _____

_____

4 There was a spider in the bath.

a _____

_____

b _____

_____

NOW TRY THIS!

- **Find a sentence from your own writing.**
- **Add words to it.**
- **Make it as long as you can.**
  Does this make it a better sentence?

Teachers' note Explain that in this activity children are going to add words to sentences. Read the completed example with them and discuss the purpose of the words added: to give information about the order in which things happened. For what other purpose could words be added? Examples include to describe Jack or the book or to say how, where or when he opened it.

A Lesson for Every Day
Literacy
7–8 Years
© A&C Black

Join-up jigsaw

- ## These words are useful for joining parts of a sentence.

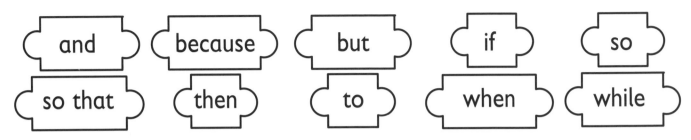

| and | because | but | if | so |
| so that | then | to | when | while |

- ## Choose a word to join these to make sentences.

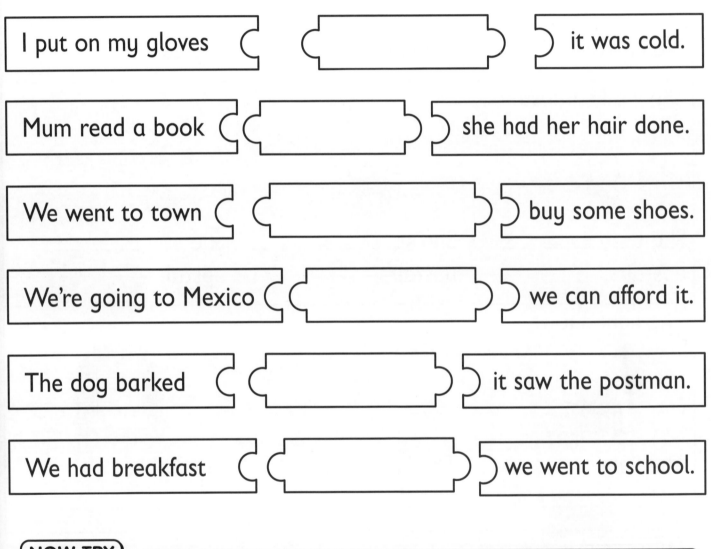

| I put on my gloves | | it was cold. |

| Mum read a book | | she had her hair done. |

| We went to town | | buy some shoes. |

| We're going to Mexico | | we can afford it. |

| The dog barked | | it saw the postman. |

| We had breakfast | | we went to school. |

NOW TRY THIS!

- ## Write four sentences using these joining words.

| and | but | so | when |

Teachers' note Remind the children of their previous work on words for joining parts of sentences. Draw out that these can simply link actions or ideas or they can say when, where or why something happened. Introduce the words in the jigsaw pieces and discuss how they are used.

A Lesson for Every Day
Literacy
7-8 Years
© A&C Black

Smart verbs

- **Read the sentences.**
- **Write a different verb to match each picture.**

He cut the carrot.

He sl _____ the carrot.

He ch _____ the carrot.

He gr _____ the carrot.

She walked upstairs.

She t _____ upstairs.

She st _____ upstairs.

She st _____ upstairs.

The light shone.

The light bl _____ .

The light tw _____ .

The light gl _____ .

NOW TRY THIS!

- **Write three different verbs for these.**

| said | ran | ate | put |

Teachers' note Remind the children that verbs are words for actions and explain that there are different verbs for the same type of action but that each one has a slightly different meaning. You could ask the children for different verbs which mean *talk*: for example, *whisper, chatter, gossip*. Ask them about the picture each one conjures up in their minds.

A Lesson for Every Day
Literacy
7–8 Years
© A&C Black

Portrait patter

- **Use this page to plan a talk about a portrait.**
- **Draw a sketch of the portrait in the box.**

Title _____

_____

Artist _____

Date (year) _____

Notes

Male/female/family/group _____

Age(s) _____

Clothes _____

_____

Why they might have chosen to wear these clothes _____

_____

_____

What they are doing _____

_____

Objects _____

_____

Why these might be in the picture _____

_____

_____

NOW TRY THIS!

- **What else can you say about the portrait?**
- **Write notes.**

Teachers' note Use this to support work in art lessons on portraits. The children could choose a portrait from a set of reproductions and say why they chose it. Alternatively, each group could talk about a portrait to discover as much as they can about the sitters, what they might want the portrait to say about them and what the artist might be saying about them.

A Lesson for Every Day
Literacy
7-8 Years
© A&C Black

Signs

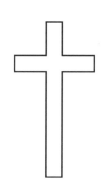

Teachers' note Give a card to each child and ask them to describe the sign to the group or class without saying what it is. They could also talk about what their sign means. The others try to draw it without seeing the card. For a less challenging activity give out copies of the page (or display it on the interactive whiteboard) and ask the class to identify the sign being described.

A Lesson for Every Day
Literacy
7–8 Years
© A&C Black

Egg challenge: 1

The great egg challenge is on!

Design a container to protect a hollow chocolate egg.
The test will be to post the egg.
It has to arrive unbroken.
Postage has to be cheap – so make
the container as light as possible.

- **First you need to do some research into containers.**
Share these tasks. Find out about:
  - egg cartons
  - containers for chocolate eggs
  - materials used for packing
  - the mail (costs and what happens to parcels).

> Work in a group of four.

> Who will do that.

My task _____

Notes for my report _____

_____

_____

_____

_____

_____

NOW TRY THIS!

- **List the three most important points in your report.**
- **Explain to your group why these points are important.**

Teachers' note Use this with 'Egg challenge: 2'. Each child needs a copy of both pages. This activity could be introduced during a design and technology lesson on the theme of 'containers'. Explain that, before designing a container to meet the challenge, the children should do some research and present their findings as a report. Discuss how and where they can find the information they need.

A Lesson for Every Day
Literacy
7-8 Years
© A&C Black

Egg challenge: 2

- **Listen to one another's reports.**
- **List the main points.**
  Write the questions _you_ asked.

Look at the speaker.
Ask questions.

Report about _____
by _____

Main points	Question
_____	_____
_____	_____
_____	_____

Report about _____
by _____

Main points	Question
_____	_____
_____	_____
_____	_____

Report about _____
by _____

Main points	Question
_____	_____
_____	_____
_____	_____

NOW TRY THIS!

- **Use what you have learned to help you design an egg container.**

Teachers' note Use this with 'Egg challenge: 1'. Model how to encourage a person to speak by inviting a volunteer to present his or her report to the class and afterwards, drawing attention to important points made by the speaker and asking questions to clarify points or to obtain further information. If possible post the eggs to school to test the challenge: do any arrive unbroken.

A Lesson for Every Day
Literacy
7-8 Years
© A&C Black

History on screen

- Watch a history programme.
- List three things you learned.
- Fill in the table to describe what you saw and heard.

Work with a partner. Notice how the programme used images and sounds.

How the programme showed this

What I learned	Someone telling it	Actors acting it	Objects	Pictures	Maps and charts
1					
2					
3					

NOW TRY THIS!

- What did you like best about the programme?
- Share your views with your group.

Teachers' note Use this to help the children to comment on a history programme they have watched. Ask them to identify three things they learned and then to think about how the programme helped them to learn these: for example, from a presenter or interviewee giving information, a re-enactment, artefacts, pictures, maps or charts.

A Lesson for Every Day
Literacy
7–8 Years
© A&C Black

Spot the scene change: 1

Form 3H watched an information programme.
They wrote a heading for each section of the programme.
They made a note of how one section ended and a new one began.

- **Circle the title of each section.**
- **Why might each section end as it does?**
  Discuss with a partner.

Title _____ The Bible _____

1 The Bible lands today
Film of the Bible lands

Voice saying Bible written here long ago.
Then picture of Bible (closed).

Moving on ⇩

2 Reading the Bible
Christians talking about when they read it

Film of girl reading Bible to herself.
Then Christians in church.

Moving on ⇩

3 In church
Minister reading from Bible

Film – Jesus talking to crowd of people.

Moving on ⇩

4 The New Testament
New Testament about story of Jesus and his teachings

Teachers' note This page provides an example of how 'Spot the change: 2' could be completed. You could use the CD-ROM to adapt it for another topic. Use it to help the children to identify and record different sections of an information broadcast and how these are linked.

A Lesson for Every Day
Literacy
7–8 Years
© A&C Black

Spot the scene change: 2

- **Watch an information programme.**
- **Write a heading for each section of the programme.**
- **Make a note of how each section moves on to the next.**

Title _____

1 _____

Moving on ⇩

2 _____

Moving on ⇩

3 _____

Moving on ⇩

4 _____

NOW TRY THIS!

- **Plan a programme about something you have learned.**
- **Use a chart.**

Work with a group.

Teachers' note It is useful first to discuss a completed version (see 'Spot the change: 1') with the children. You could present the example as a record of a programme some children watched, or you could use an adapted version, based on an information programme you and the children have watched. They can then complete this page after watching another programme.

A Lesson for Every Day
Literacy
7–8 Years
© A&C Black

Make a note

• Help Pilar to write notes **about centipedes and millipedes.**

How are centipedes and millipedes alike, and how are they different?

Centipedes

Centipedes have long bodies with many segments. There is a pair of legs on each segment except the one behind the head and the two tail segments. The most common centipede in Britain has 15 segments and 15 pairs of legs. It has a glossy brown colour and grows up to three centimetres long. It has a pair of long feelers on its head and two strong pincers just below the head. These are poisonous. The centipede uses them to kill worms and insects for food and animals that try to eat it. Its bite does not usually harm humans. It lives in damp places where there is soil.

Millipedes

Millipedes have long bodies with many segments. There are two pairs of legs on each segment except the two behind the head; these have one pair of legs. A common millipede in Britain is the black millipede, which has about 50 segments and 96 legs. It is black and grows up to about two centimetres long. On its head it has a pair of feelers. The millipede lives in damp rotting plant material and that is what it eats. It can also burrow into soil. It curls into a ball to protect itself.

	centipede	millipede
body		
head		
legs		
length		
food		
habitat		
protecting itself		

Teachers' note As a shared activity the children could try completing the first two or three rows of the chart without re-reading the passage. Demonstrate that it can be difficult to remember everything that has been read. Explain that a chart helps with this because it uses very brief notes and is easy to read quickly to find information.

A Lesson for Every Day
Literacy
7-8 Years
© A&C Black

A non-chronological report

- **Underline the** main points **.**
- **Help Malik the Martian to write** notes **.**

Earthlings

There are many types of Earthling. They come in all kinds of shapes, colours and sizes.

Body Earthlings usually have four legs. They use two of these for walking and the other two for feeding and pressing buttons on keyboards. They have only one head with no feelers.

Movement They can walk but most of them move around in metal boxes on wheels. They line their wheeled boxes behind one another on roads and sometimes stay there for several hours without moving. Then they shout at one another until the line of wheeled boxes begins to move.

Diet The food of Earthlings comes from plants or animals. Much of it is in boxes, which they collect from large buildings in their wheeled boxes.

Young Earthlets are similar to their parents but smaller. They have little hair and no teeth when they are born and they cannot walk.

Habitat Earthlings live in boxes. Some live in colonies but others live alone. The size of the box does not always match the size of the colony.

Earthlings

Many types. All shapes, sizes, colours.

Body: 4 legs – 2 for walking, 2 for pressing buttons.

1 head – 0 feelers.

Movement:

Teachers' note Tell the children that this is from an imaginary information book about Earthlings written for children on Mars. Point out the main features of the sample notes: unimportant words are missed out, some words are shortened and notes are not written in sentences. Show how headings can help.

A Lesson for Every Day
Literacy
7-8 Years
© A&C Black

Sentences from notes

- **Read the** notes **about rich and poor children in Tudor times.**
- **Use each note to help you to write a** sentence **.**

Work in a group.

Notes	Sentences
Poor – age 4 work on farms + at home	
Not many toys – rich or poor Rich girls – dolls	
Rich – pets: dogs, monkey, bird Poor – cat to kill mice	
Age 7 – rich boys → grammar school, then university at 15 Latin + Religion	
Not many girls at school – learned how to manage home	
Poor – toys made from bits of wood, bone, stone	
Poor boys – age 7 – no school or church school → reading + simple maths	
Quite well-off boys – apprenticed to learn trade. Parents had to pay	

NOW TRY THIS!

- **Cut out and sort the sentences into sets to make** paragraphs **.**

Teachers' note Copy this page onto A3 paper. Model the first sentence: *This is about poor children, how young they are when they begin to work and the kind of work they might do, so I'll write 'Poor children work on farms and at home from four years old.'* Then, perhaps, I'll add 'some' because some poor children might do other work or begin when they are older.

A Lesson for Every Day
Literacy
7–8 Years
© A&C Black

Report from sentences

- **Read the** sentences **you wrote about Tudor children.**
- **Use them to help you to complete this** report **.**

Rich and poor children in Tudor times

In Tudor times not all children went to school. Most girls _____ _____ . Instead _____ _____

School for poor children

When they were seven years old rich boys went to _____ .
They learned _____ .
Then _____ .

When they were seven some poor boys _____ , others _____ .
Boys from quite well-off families _____

_____ .

There were no toy shops. Poor children _____

_____ . Rich _____ .

Poor families kept animals for food or because they were useful. As well as being pets _____ . But children from rich families

_____ .

NOW TRY THIS!

- **Read the report with a friend.**
- **See if you can improve it.**

Teachers' note Ask the children to reread their sentences from 'Sentences from notes' and ask them to use the information in them to help them to complete this report. Ask them to notice how the sentences have been grouped into paragraphs that are linked by topic: girls, rich boys, poor boys, toys, pets.

A Lesson for Every Day
Literacy
7–8 Years
© A&C Black

Monster report

- **Plan a** report **about a type of monster in fairytales, myths and legends.**
- **Write** notes **in the paragraph boxes.**

Heading _____

What the monster looks like

_____

_____

Stories it is in

_____

_____

What it does

_____

_____

Where it lives, and why

_____

_____

NOW TRY THIS!

- **Write your report in four** paragraphs .

Teachers' note The children first need opportunities to discuss the monsters in fairytales, myths and legends they have read. Ask them to list the monsters in groups according to type and then to choose one type of monster to write about, using the paragraph headings provided.

A Lesson for Every Day
Literacy
7–8 Years
© A&C Black

Three sets

- **Work in a group.**
- **Cut out and sort the** sentences **into three sets.**
- **Explain how you sorted the sentences.**

Most wood is strong, so it is good for building.	Wood is a natural material.
Natural materials have not been made by people.	It is difficult to push a drawing pin or knock a nail into hard wood.
Some parts of buildings that can be made of wood are doors, floors, window frames and beams to support roofs and floors.	Some large everyday things we use that can be made of wood are chairs, tables, shelves, beds and cupboards.
Some small everyday things we use that can be made of wood are pencils, rulers, spoons, boxes and handles.	It comes from the trunks and branches of trees.
Some woods are harder than others.	Pine and balsa are soft woods.
Oak and ebony are hard woods.	It is easy to push a drawing pin or knock a nail into soft wood.
Soft wood is easy to cut.	Natural materials come from animals, plants and the earth.
Some of these wooden objects could be made from other materials.	Rulers, spoons, boxes and handles can also be made from plastic.

Teachers' note Tell the children that these sentences come from a non-chronological report about wood and ask them to work together to sort them into sets that belong together. They should be able to say why they belong together.

A Lesson for Every Day
Literacy
7-8 Years
© A&C Black

131

Paragraph boxes

- **Read the children's** notes **about their local area.**
- **Use them to help you to write** sentences **about it.**
- **Write each sentence in the correct box.**

village is in valley – pastures
river runs through
one shop (post office + general store)

old sawmill still working
but no mill wheel now
farms all around: sheep + cattle

one pub
village hall next to pub
two bridges over river

main road through village
not very busy
hills all around
woodland on hills

Natural features

○ _____
_____
_____

Human features

○ _____
_____
_____
_____
_____

Teachers' note Explain that the notes were made by children as they walked around their local area and that, back at school, these notes need to be organised into paragraphs on natural features and human features. Discuss what is meant by natural features and human features (link this with work in geography).

A Lesson for Every Day
Literacy
7-8 Years
© A&C Black

Report plan

- **Look at the pictures and read the** notes.
- **Write a** report **about sheep, their teeth and what they eat.**

wool covers skin

mammal (babies born
live, feeds them on milk)

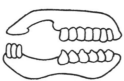

4 legs

feeds on grass
has to eat a lot

Sheep

_____

_____

Sheep's teeth

_____

_____

What sheep eat

_____

_____

NOW TRY THIS!

- **Find out about another animal.**
- **Write a report about the animal, its teeth and what it eats.**

Make three paragraphs.

Teachers' note The children are given the topic for each paragraph. Ask them to read the headings and write the notes as sentences in the right paragraphs.

A Lesson for Every Day
Literacy
7-8 Years
© A&C Black

Report improver

- **Work with a partner.**
- **Which parts of the** report **can you improve?**
- **Underline them.**
- **Rewrite the report.**

Write better sentences.
Use connectives.

Magic spells in stories

There are magic spells in a lot of stories like *Cinderella* the fairy turns a pumpkin into a coach and mice into horses and lizards into footmen and old rags into a lovely ball gown. There are three main types of magic spell and one type of spell is to change a person or animal into something else and another is to give them special skills like flying or being invisible and the third type is to protect them from harm. One way of casting a spell is to say magic words and sometimes this works better with a magic mixture. Give the person a magic object and tell them some magic words to say. Wave a magic wand. There are different ways to stop a spell you can say magic words or do something special like spinning around anticlockwise while looking at the moon. Or the spell might be set to wear off at a special time like in *Cinderella* it was midnight.

_____
_____
_____
_____
_____
_____
_____
_____
_____
_____
_____
_____
_____

Teachers' note Ask the children to read the entire report and to mark the end of each paragraph. They should then decide whether any sentences need to be moved before they begin to read each sentence closely to see if they can write it in a better way.

A Lesson for Every Day
Literacy
7-8 Years
© A&C Black

Go with the flow

- **Read the sentences.**
- **Join them with** time words **.**
- **Write the long sentences you have made.**

You might have to change the capital letters and full stops.

| As soon as | → | Santa Claus woke up. He knew it was Christmas Eve. |

Time-bank

as soon as

first

then

while

_____

_____

| | → | He fed his reindeer. |

| He ate a healthy breakfast. | ← | |

_____

_____

| | | The elves began to wrap the toys. Santa got out his red suit. |

_____

_____

NOW TRY THIS!

- **Write three sentences about Santa Claus.**
- **Use these** time words **.**

  meanwhile   next   when

Teachers' note Remind the children of the purposes of different words in sentences: to say what someone or something does/did (verb), to name something (noun), to replace a noun (pronoun) or to say where, when or how something happened. Ask which would be the most useful type of word when putting the events of a story in order (words to say when something happened).

A Lesson for Every Day
Literacy
7–8 Years
© A&C Black

These sentences are from a report.

- **Underline the** verbs .
- **Circle the** pronouns :

(I) (me) (we) (us) (you) (he) (him) (she) (her) (it) (they) (them)

Plants are living things.

They make their own food.

They need air, water, and sunshine.

Some plants grow in shady places but they need some light.

Animals are living things.

They have to find food to eat.

A sunflower

- **Tick the correct answers.**

    The sentences are in the past ☐ tense.

    present ☐

    They are in the first ☐ person.

    second ☐

    third ☐

NOW TRY THIS!

- **Write three sentences about plants you know.**
- **Use the** present **tense and the** third **person.**

Teachers' note Revise previous work on verbs and person. Ask children what they know about verbs and remind them of the past and present tenses. Also remind them about the pronouns and verb forms used in the first and third person. Draw out that non-chronological reports are usually written in the present tense and in the third person.

A Lesson for Every Day
Literacy
7–8 Years
© A&C Black

Picture this: 1

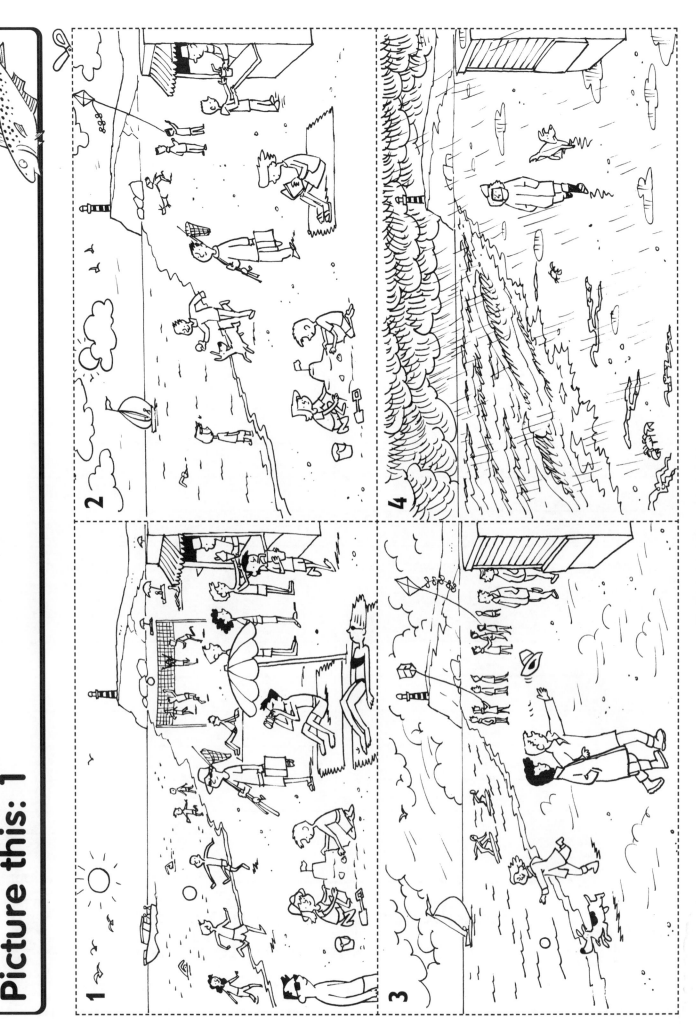

Teachers' note This page can be used in different ways: for example, give one child in each group a picture to describe to the others, who should draw it – during another lesson it could be the turn of a different child to describe a picture. Compare the children's drawings with the original and discuss how any differences arose. See also 'Picture this: 2'.

A Lesson for Every Day
Literacy
7–8 Years
© A&C Black

137

Picture this: 2

- **Make notes on how to describe a picture to a partner.**
- **You will have one minute for talking.**

Think about how to help your partner to picture the scene.

I am describing picture number _____

The setting – the landscape, natural and built features	The season and weather – and how you can tell
_____	_____
_____	_____
_____	_____
_____	_____
_____	_____
The people – what they are wearing and what they are doing	**Any animals – what they are doing**
_____	_____
_____	_____
_____	_____
_____	_____

Talk about ways of improving your description.

NOW TRY THIS!

- **Describe the picture to a partner.**
- **Your partner should try to draw it.**
- **Compare the drawing with the picture.**

Teachers' note Use this with 'Picture this: 1' to help the children to make their description as accurate as possible and to plan their description before they speak to their group. It might help if they compare the pictures and focus on the differences. Afterwards the listeners in the group could compile a list of words the speaker used that they thought were good (see the notes on the activity on page XX).

A Lesson for Every Day
Literacy
7–8 Years
© A&C Black

Jumble sale

Class 3 are having a jumble sale.

We need to ask people to bring things to sell.

Three people can look after each stall.

We need tables.

- **What do the children need to do?**
  Talk to your group.
  Write a list.

Work in a group.

Jumble sale – things to do

_____

_____

_____

_____

_____

_____

_____

_____

_____

_____

_____

NOW TRY THIS!

- **What should the children do first?**
  Write out the list in the correct order.

Teachers' note This could be used in connection with any event the children are going to organise, such as money-raising effort for charity. This provides support during the planning stage in which the children identify the tasks. During another lesson, the children could decide how to allocate the tasks among the class.

A Lesson for Every Day
Literacy
7-8 Years
© A&C Black

Our school grounds

- **What do you think of your school grounds?**
- **Talk about the 'buzz points' and write your answers like this:**

We agree, because …   We disagree, because …
We are not sure, because …

Work with a group.

There are plenty of lovely plants.

_____
_____
_____

We need more trees.

_____
_____
_____

There is plenty to do.

_____
_____
_____

The grounds look scruffy.

_____
_____
_____

The grounds are safe.

_____
_____
_____

NOW TRY THIS!

- **Think and talk together and write a 'buzz point' of your own to discuss.**

Teachers' note Tell the children that they are going to look at the school grounds and discuss some 'buzz points' then record what their group agrees. They should decide whether they agree with each point or are unsure. After sharing their views with other groups they might make up their minds about the 'unsure' points or even change their minds about others.

A Lesson for Every Day
Literacy
7–8 Years
© A&C Black

I disagree

- **Read the discussions.**
- **How can the children disagree politely?**
- **Write in the speech bubbles.**

Work with a partner.

We're going to make cheese sandwiches.

No, we're not. I hate them.

Well – what do you want then?

No one's had any good ideas, so far.

I did. I told you what we've got to do. The playground needs a bench.

No. That's rubbish! We won't use it.

NOW TRY THIS!

- **Make a 'disagreement words' bank.**

Teachers' note The children could work with a partner to discuss what is wrong with the way the children in the pictures express their views and to decide how to do this politely. They could then read the new dialogue aloud to others in their group and listen to them doing the same.

A Lesson for Every Day
Literacy
7–8 Years
© A&C Black

Base words with the suffix tion

- **Write the** base words **next to the** tion **words.**
- **Tell a partner what happens when the suffix** tion **is added.**

One has been done for you.

- **Underline the base word letters that change when** tion **is added.**

tion word	Base word
information	inform
subtraction	
quotation	
creation	
decoration	
action	
invention	
pollution	
instruction	
direction	
multiplication	
celebration	
observation	

Base word bank

act
celebrate
create
decorate
direct
inform
instruct
invent
multiply
observe
pollute
quote
subtract

NOW TRY THIS!

- **Write these base words.**
- **Add the suffix** tion **and write the new words.**

introduce   relate   describe   compete

142

Teachers' note Introduce or revise the base word and suffix using familiar examples such as *call/called, dust/duster, fun/funny*. Read the completed example with the children and ask how *inform* was different before the suffix was added. Ensure that they know that **ti** in the suffix represents /**sh**/.

A Lesson for Every Day
Literacy
7–8 Years
© A&C Black

Making sense with sion

- **Add the suffix** sion **to the base word in bold type.**
- **Write the new word in the box.**
- **Tell a friend how the base word changed.**

We are going to watch **televise** ☐ later.

I made the **decide** ☐ to work hard at school.

The builders are building an **extend** ☐ on our house.

There was a mid-air **collide** ☐ between two planes.

Emily had a puzzled **express** ☐ on her face.

There was a loud **explode** ☐ and flames shot into the air.

Simon said he had a **confess** ☐ to make: he broke the window.

The opposite of multiplication is **divide** ☐.

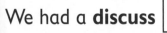

There was a lot of **confuse** ☐ about what to do.

We had a **discuss** ☐ about school rules.

NOW TRY THIS!

- **Add the suffix** sion **to these words.**

  admit   permit   revise

  Use a dictionary.

- **Write a sentence using the base word and another sentence using the** sion **word.**

Teachers' note Introduce or revise base word and suffix using familiar examples such as *love/lovely*, *tap/tapped*, *sing/singer*. Ensure that the children know that **si** in the suffix represents /zh/ (*television*) and that **ss** represents /sh/ (*discussion*).

A Lesson for Every Day
Literacy
7–8 Years
© A&C Black

It's like this

- **Add the suffix** `like` **to make words that mean these.**

 Do the base words change?

like a child	like a lady	like a stick
like a slug	like a bead	like a tree
busy getting things done, like a business	like glue	like straw
like a cat	like a nation at war	like a cow

NOW TRY THIS!

- **Write sentences using three of the words as adjectives to describe people or objects.**

Teachers' note Begin with a sentence using the phrase *like a …* to describe something: for example, *We saw an enormous animal like a bear.* Then help the children to make *like a bear* into an adjective using the suffix **-like**: *We saw an enormous bearlike animal.* Repeat this using *like a peg, like a snail.* Ask the children to notice if the base word changes when **-like** is added.

A Lesson for Every Day
Literacy
7–8 Years
© A&C Black

Words with usefulness

- **Add the suffix** `ness` **to make a word that makes sense.**
- **Write the new word and cross out the base word.**

> The last letter of the base word may need to change.

> I am crying with sad _____ .

> I hope you'll soon smile with happy _____ .

> Your work is poor because of your lazy _____ .

> She was absent from school because of her ill _____ .

> Our class won a prize for neat _____ and tidy _____ .

> I like Liam for his good _____ and kind _____ .

> I could taste the sweet _____ of sugar and the salty _____ of crisps.

> I could taste the sour _____ of lemon and the bitter _____ of coffee.

- **What changes do you notice in the base word?**

NOW TRY THIS!

- **What kind of words can you add** `ness` **to?**
- **Write three other examples.**
- **Use the base words in sentences.**
- **Use the** `ness` **words in sentences.**

Teachers' note Ask if the sentence in the first example makes sense. Can the children make another word, using *sad* as the base word, that makes sense? They could say what each of these words does in a sentence (*sad* is an adjective that describes someone or something; *sadness* is a noun – the name of a feeling).

A Lesson for Every Day
Literacy
7–8 Years
© A&C Black

Opposites with [il], [im] or [in]

- **Add the prefix [il], [im] or [in] to make the opposite of the word in bold type.**

I am **mortal**. That means that one day I shall die.

I am _____. That means that I shall not die.

It is **legal** to park in this street. That means you are allowed to park here.

It is _____ to park in this street. That means you are not allowed to park here.

Most insects are **visible** to the naked eye. That means you can see them without a microscope.

Germs are _____ to the naked eye. That means you can't see them without a microscope.

My laptop is **perfect**. That means there is nothing wrong with it.

My iPod is _____. That means there is something wrong with it.

NOW TRY THIS!

- **Write six more words that take the prefix [il], [im] or [in] for their opposite meanings.**

146

Teachers' note Provide dictionaries. Read the first example and model how to choose the appropriate prefix: 'ilmortal and inmortal sound odd, but immortal sounds right. I'll check that in the dictionary [do so] … yes, immortal means not mortal'. Ask how the prefix alters the meaning of the word. Does the spelling of the base word change?

A Lesson for Every Day
Literacy
7–8 Years
© A&C Black

All wrong

- **Match each definition to a word with the prefix** | mis |.
- **Write the** | mis | **word in the box.**

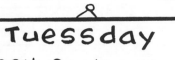
1 Something that doesn't fit

2 To give wrong directions

Tuessday
29th Septender

5 Spell wrongly

3 To match things wrongly

6 To give wrong information

4 Wrongly shaped

7 To understand wrongly

NOW TRY THIS!

- **Write three other words with the prefix** | mis |.
- **Write definitions for them.**
- **What does** | mis | **mean?**

| Mis | at the beginning of a word is not always a prefix.

Teachers' note Read the first example with the children and ask them to find the word in the *mis* words that best fits the definition. Ask how the prefix **mis-** alters the meaning of the word and whether the spelling of the base word changes. It is useful to point out that **mis-** at the beginning of a word might not be a prefix: for example, *miserable, miser, miss.*

A Lesson for Every Day
Literacy
7–8 Years
© A&C Black

Prefix pre

- **Match the words with the prefix** pre **to the definitions.**
- **Write the words on the chart.**

> precooked   predict   prefix   preheat   prehistoric
> prepare   prepay   preschool   preset   preview

Word	Definition
	Before starting school.
	A look at something before most people see it.
	To say what is going to happen in the future.
	To pay for something before you get it or do it.
	Cooked before you need it.
	A group of letters added to the beginning of a word.
	To get ready before an event.
	To set something before you need it to be done: for example, a DVD recorder.
	To heat something before you need it.
	A very long time ago – before history.

- **What do you think** pre **means?**

NOW TRY THIS!

- **List the base words from above.**
- **Put a line through any that are not real words.**

> The ones that are not real words come from another language – Latin.

Teachers' note Write up the word *prefix* and underline **pre**. Explain that **pre** is a prefix and ask the children to give a definition of *prefix* (a group of letters fixed to the beginning of a word). What do they think *suffix* means? Tell them that some base words come from other languages, such as Latin or Greek, and so their meanings might not be obvious.

A Lesson for Every Day
Literacy
7-8 Years
© A&C Black

Xword

- **Match the definitions to the words with the prefix** `ex`.
- **Write the answers on the crossword.**

Answers

exceed	excursion	exit	expel	extra
except	exile	expand	explore	extract

Clues: across

2 A trip away from home (9)
4 Go outside the limit (6)
6 A way out (4)
7 To spread out (6)
9 To take out (7)
10 Apart from (6)

Down

1 To send out (5)
3 Outside the normal amount (5)
5 Find out about (7)
8 Someone who has been sent away (5)

- **What do you think the prefix** `ex` **means?**

NOW TRY THIS!

- **Write two other words that have the prefix** `ex`.
- **Write sentences to show their meanings.**

Teachers' note Explain crossword conventions (see the notes on the activity on page 18). During the plenary session, invite feedback about the meaning of **ex-** and note that it can have other meanings: for instance, 'no longer' or 'former', as in ex-husband, ex-president or ex-wife.

A Lesson for Every Day
Literacy
7-8 Years
© A&C Black

Watch and note

Mair watched *Be a Magician*.

- **Read her notes about a magic trick.**
- **Write the** `instructions` **.**

The magic handkerchief

Say 2 can stand on h'chief w'out being able
to touch one another. Both feet on h'chief. door
H'chief floor in doorway.
Close door
Tell I to stand on I end.
Tell other to st. on oth. end.
Ask if can touch one another.
No – cos door in way.

h'chief

_____   _____

_____   _____

_____   _____

_____   _____

_____   _____

_____   _____

NOW TRY THIS!

- **Try the trick.**
- **See if you can improve the instructions.**

Are any more rules needed?

Teachers' note The children could talk about television programmes they have watched which tell them how to make and do something. Do they remember the instructions? Tell them that this page shows how someone made notes quickly during a programme so as not to forget. Their task is to turn the notes into instructions for someone else to follow.

A Lesson for Every Day
Literacy
7–8 Years
© A&C Black

Make it

- **Put the** `instructions` **in order.**
- **Number them.**
- **Write or draw anything that is missing.**
- **Glue the instructions onto a piece of paper.**

Carefully cover the card with the sheet of transparent plastic.

Pour a tablespoonful of iron filings on to the centre of the card.

You could photograph the different faces you make.

Tape the edges with sticky tape so that the iron filings cannot drop out.

Use a magnet to pull iron filings into place to make hair, eyebrows and so on.

Draw a large face on the piece of white card. Do not draw any hair, eyebrows, moustache or beard.

NOW TRY THIS!

- **Test the instructions.**
- **Write a report about how easy they are to follow.**

Teachers' note Remind the children of the sentence structure of instructions (they usually begin with a verb and are written as commands). Compare this with the sentence structure of a recount or non-chronological report. Point out that instructions should be written step-by-step in the correct order to help the reader to do or make something.

A Lesson for Every Day
Literacy
7–8 Years
© A&C Black

- **Think how to change the** recount **to** instructions .
- **Underline the words to change.**

A frothy explosion

This is what I used: bicarbonate of soda, vinegar, funnel, dessert spoon, plastic bottle, cork to fit the bottle.

I did this outdoors because it is messy and dangerous.

I put the funnel into the top of the bottle.

bicarbonate of soda

Then I poured in 4 dessert spoonfuls of bicarbonate of soda.

vinegar

Next I poured in ten dessert spoonfuls of vinegar.

cork

Immediately I pushed in the cork.

Then I stood well back. ⚠

Teachers' note Use this with 'Recount to instruction: 2'. Ask the children to read this page and to say whether it gives instructions, a report about something or a recount of what was done. Ask them how they can tell, and draw attention to the person in which it is written and the tense of the verbs. If they try this practically, close supervision is needed!

A Lesson for Every Day
Literacy
7–8 Years
© A&C Black

- **Write** instructions **for 'A frothy explosion'.**
- **Draw diagrams to help.**
- **Write labels.**

Heading _____

Materials   **Equipment**

1 _____

_____

2 _____

_____

3 _____

_____

4 _____

_____

5 _____

_____

6 _____

_____

Teachers' note Use this with 'Recount to instruction: 1'. Ask the children to re-write the recount as instructions that tell the reader what to do rather than recount what someone did. They could test their instructions. For safety you could demonstrate the final stage. Note the importance of safety warnings in some instructions.

A Lesson for Every Day
Literacy
7–8 Years
© A&C Black

The instructions judge

- **Test a set of** instructions .
- **Give the instructions a score for each question.**
- **Write your reasons.**

 Colour the towers.

 The highest score is 5.

Intructions for _____

How easy were they to read?
| 5 |
| 4 |
| 3 |
| 2 |
| 1 |
_____
_____
_____
_____

How easy were they to understand?
| 5 |
| 4 |
| 3 |
| 2 |
| 1 |
_____
_____
_____
_____

How good were the illustrations?
| 5 |
| 4 |
| 3 |
| 2 |
| 1 |
_____
_____
_____
_____

How well were they put in order?
| 5 |
| 4 |
| 3 |
| 2 |
| 1 |
_____
_____
_____
_____

 **NOW TRY THIS!**

- **Write your own instructions for the same purpose.**

Teachers' note Different groups could use this page to evaluate different sets of instructions. Provide instructions for things they could make or do so that the evaluation can be based on real testing.

A Lesson for Every Day
Literacy
7–8 Years
© A&C Black

Step by step

- **Watch a recording about making something.**
- **List the things you need.**
- **Write** notes **about what to do.**

Replay it if you need to.

Write as many steps as you need.

Things you need

Step 1 → **Step 2** → **Step 3**

Step 5 ← **Step 4**

Step 6 → **Step 7** → **Step 8**

Step 10 ← **Step 9**

NOW TRY THIS!

- **Write** instructions **from your notes.**
- **Add any** diagrams **or pictures that will help.**

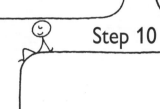

Teachers' note First select a suitable television recording showing how to make or do something. You could try the BBC children's website, particularly *Blue Peter*, which includes several short recordings. The children will probably need to watch more than once in order to make a note of everything.

A Lesson for Every Day
Literacy
7-8 Years
© A&C Black

Snap!

- **With a friend, discuss how to play 'Snap!'**
- **Write notes for the main** <u>instructions</u> **in the boxes.**
- **Cut them out and put them in order.**

The questions will help.

What happens when a player says 'Snap'?	How do you know when the game has finished?
How do you win?	How many cards do you deal?
What do you do before you deal?	What do the players do with their cards?
When do you say 'Snap'?	Who goes first?

NOW TRY THIS!

- **Write instructions for playing 'Snap!'**

Teachers' note The children might need to play the game of Snap! to refresh their memories. Ask them to make notes in the boxes – these need not be written in sentences.

A Lesson for Every Day
Literacy
7-8 Years
© A&C Black

The witches' spell

- **Read what the witches and the cats say about a new spell.**
- **Write** **instructions** **for other witches to follow.**

We said together, "Abracadabra – all teachers be cats!"

We have turned all teachers into cats! Ha, ha, ha!

You all waved your wands up and down three times.

We began by eating a tin of cat food each.

Then we walked three times anti-clockwise around a tree with catkins.

There had to be four witches.

It had to be done at night by the light of a full moon.

The last thing you did was to bury some old fish bones under the tree.

How to _____

You need

4 witches with wands _____   _____

_____   _____

1 Choose a night with a full moon. _____

2 _____

3 _____

4 _____

5 _____

6 _____

Teachers' note The children should focus on the language of instructions: changing the verbs to the imperative form (although this term will probably not be introduced). You could ask them first to underline the words they need to change and remind them of the need to set out at the start what will be needed.

A Lesson for Every Day
Literacy
7-8 Years
© **A&C Black**

157

Do this

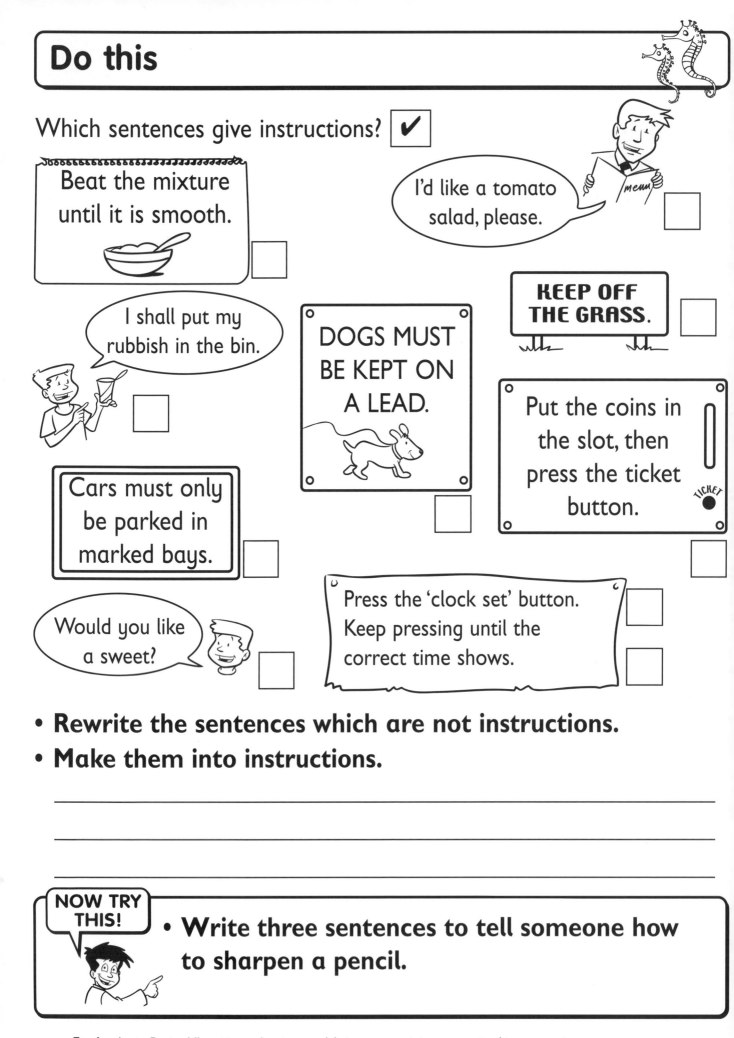

Which sentences give instructions? ✔

Beat the mixture until it is smooth.

I'd like a tomato salad, please.

KEEP OFF THE GRASS.

I shall put my rubbish in the bin.

DOGS MUST BE KEPT ON A LEAD.

Put the coins in the slot, then press the ticket button.

Cars must only be parked in marked bays.

Press the 'clock set' button. Keep pressing until the correct time shows.

Would you like a sweet?

- **Rewrite the sentences which are not instructions.**
- **Make them into instructions.**

_____

_____

_____

NOW TRY THIS!

- **Write three sentences to tell someone how to sharpen a pencil.**

Teachers' note Revise different types of sentence and their purposes: giving a recount, asking a question, giving information, giving instructions. Read the first example with the children and ask what kind of sentence it is. Draw out that it is an instruction because it tells the listener or reader what to do. Point out how the verb differs from the verb in a story or information sentence or a question.

A Lesson for Every Day
Literacy
7–8 Years
© A&C Black

Command verbs

- **In the boxes write** verbs **that give** instructions .

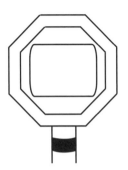

PLEASE

YOUR FEET

right at the
corner.

PLEASE

BELL FOR
SERVICE

DANGER
DO NOT

OF THE DOG

1   the butter and sugar.

2   the eggs.

ROAD WORKS

SLOWLY

PLEASE

HANDRAIL

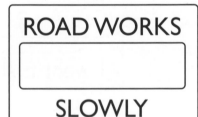
left at the lights then

straight on to the top
of the hill.

NOW TRY THIS!

- **Look for instruction verbs in your classroom.**
- **List six instructions.**
- **Draw boxes around the** verbs .

Teachers' note Remind the children of their previous work on instructions and verbs. Ask what they know about the verb in an instruction sentence. Complete the first example with them by asking them if they know what the object is (a road sign). Ask what they might see written on a sign which has this shape (Stop). Point out that Stop is an instruction or command.

A Lesson for Every Day
Literacy
7-8 Years
© **A&C Black**

That's the way

Ellie is talking about her journey to school.

- **Change each sentence to an instruction.**
- **Circle the words you will change.**
- **Rewrite the sentence.**

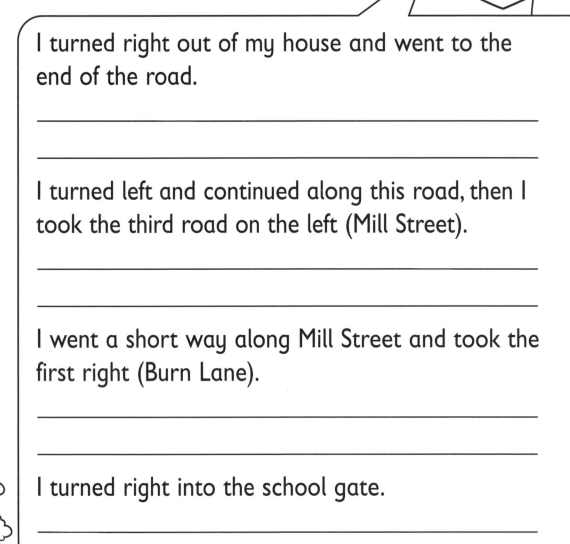

I turned right out of my house and went to the end of the road.

_____

_____

I turned left and continued along this road, then I took the third road on the left (Mill Street).

_____

_____

I went a short way along Mill Street and took the first right (Burn Lane).

_____

_____

I turned right into the school gate.

_____

- **Write three instruction sentences to give directions to somewhere you know.**

Teachers' note Read the first example with the children and ask then what kind of sentence this is: question, instruction, information or recount. How can they tell? Focus on the verb: note that it is in the past tense and that it says what the writer did. It is a recount (story sentence). Discuss how it could be changed into an instruction to tell someone how to find their way.

A Lesson for Every Day
Literacy
7–8 Years
© A&C Black

Ancient Egyptians: 1

The kingdom

(in north east Africa)

About 3200 BC King Menes of Upper Egypt conquered Lower Egypt.

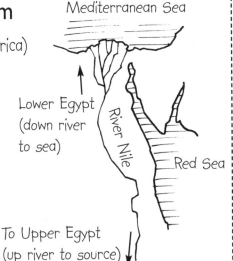

Mediterranean Sea

Lower Egypt (down river to sea)

River Nile

Red Sea

To Upper Egypt (up river to source)

The Nile

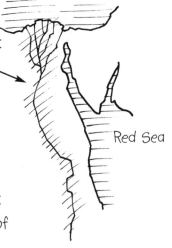

Mediterranean Sea

Area that usually flooded.

Red Sea

Floods left mud – good for the land.

One year all this part flooded, in the reign of Pharaoh Amhep II.

Pharaohs

Pharaoh had to marry princess. Could even be sister, granddaughter or other relation.

Festival of Heb-sed – pharaoh proved he was fit – ran round special course.

Made offerings to gods – 'Make Nile flood'. If not, he was blamed.

Peasants

Owned by land-owner.

Had to farm land. Pharaoh took a share of crop, so did land-owner. Not much left for peasants.

Gods

Main god Osiris – god of death. In charge of Earth.

Isis – wife of Osiris. In charge of women and children.

Anubis – head of jackal. In charge of mummies and the dead.

Pyramids

Built from huge slabs of stone.

Burial chamber inside. Entrance sealed.

Pharaoh buried inside with riches – jewels, ornaments, also food for journey to underworld.

Inside walls had stories of pharaoh's life written on them.

Teachers' note Cut out the cards on this page and on 'Ancient Egyptians: 2' and give one to each child. Those with copies of the same card could work together to decide what information about the topic the card provides. Ask them to write sentences about this so that they can tell another group. Continued on 'Ancient Egyptians: 2'.

A Lesson for Every Day
Literacy
7-8 Years
© A&C Black

Ancient Egyptians: 2

Mummies

Brain and innards taken out. Heart left in.

Body dried out with salt called natron.

Stuffed with linen cloth.

Wrapped in layers of bandage.

Put in coffin.

Grave robbers

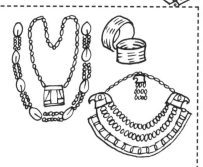

Almost all pyramids robbed.

Robbers knew they would find jewels and other riches there.

If caught – tortured or had head chopped off.

Tried to hide crime by sealing up pyramid afterwards.

Writing

Hieroglyphs – picture writing.

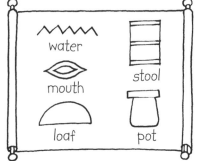

water
mouth
loaf
stool
pot

Took archaeologists a long time to work out all the symbols.

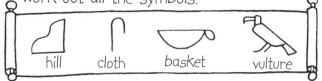

hill   cloth   basket   vulture

Counting and measuring

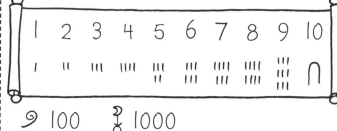

1 2 3 4 5 6 7 8 9 10

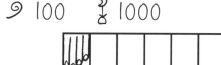

100   1000

1 cubit

4 digits = 1 palm. 7 palms = 1 cubit

Clothes

peasants   rich people

Children

Ball made from vegetable fibre.

Glazed top made of mixture of materials bound together.

Wooden lion. The jaw opens when you pull string.

Teachers' note Once the children have planned what they will say, they can share the information by 'jigsawing': children with the same cards sit together in groups, and one from each group visits another group to present the information. They then listen to someone in that group presenting theirs and return to their own group to share what they have heard.

A Lesson for Every Day
Literacy
7–8 Years
© A&C Black

The root of the matter

- **Discuss this question.**

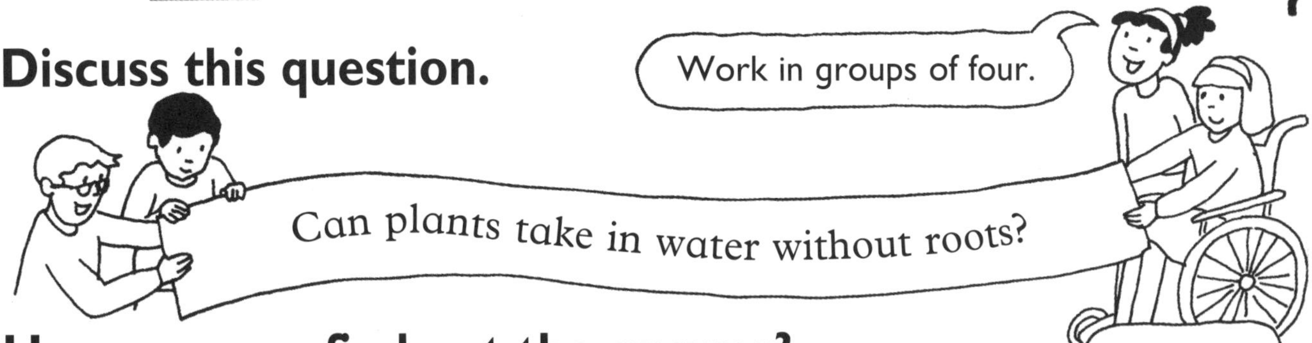

Work in groups of four.

Can plants take in water without roots?

- **How can you find out the answer?**
  Listen to everyone's ideas.
  Make notes on the pot plants.

Who will do the writing?

- **What do you think will be the answer?**
  How will you know if you are right?
  What will you do? Who will do what?

NOW TRY THIS!

- **Try out your experiment**

Teachers' note Emphasise that everyone in the group should have an opportunity to speak and should listen carefully to each other's ideas. When it is their turn to speak, if someone else has had the same idea they can add to what has already been said.

A Lesson for Every Day
Literacy
7–8 Years
© A&C Black

A good discussion

This group of children are having a discussion. How well are they doing?

Harry

Ellie

Ellie, I'd like to know...

That was interesting, Ellie. Can you tell us more about...

I wonder what they are doing over there...

Sonali

Connor

- ## Work with a partner.
- ## Fill in the report form.

Discussion report		
Name	Good points	Bad points

NOW TRY THIS!

- ## Write a letter to the group. Tell them what they do well and how they can improve.

Teachers' note Remind the children about how to hold a discussion and ask them to think about their rules for good discussions. The children should work in pairs and then share their responses with their groups or with the class. Discuss how the actions of the children in the picture help or hinder the discussion. Point out that boxes on the chart can be left blank if there are no obvious good/bad points.

A Lesson for Every Day
Literacy
7-8 Years
© A&C Black

Persuaders

- **What do these try to persuade people to do?**
- **Write on the charts.**

①  Taste the rich toffee

② Fabulous Funfair. Three for the price of two.

③ Cigarettes kill.

④ 16th April

Dear Sir

I am sending this phone back because the battery will not charge. I would like a new phone as this one is not fit for its purpose.

⑤ SAVE THE EARTH
- RECYCLE
- RE-USE
- SWITCH OFF

Source	What it persuades people to do
1	
2	
3	
4	
5	

NOW TRY THIS!

- **Explain *how* each source tries to persuade.**

Teachers' note You could begin by using the interactive whiteboard to present some Internet, television and magazine or newspaper advertisements. Ask the children what each one is advertising and how it persuades its audience to do or buy something: giving reasons, appealing to senses, giving special offers and so on.

A Lesson for Every Day
Literacy
7-8 Years
© A&C Black

No-cook chocolate slice: 1

- **Work with a partner.**
- **Take it in turns to tell one another how to make no-cook chocolate slice.**

Ingredients		Steps

150g digestive biscuits

50g rolled oats

50g raisins

25g chopped apricots

50g blueberries + cranberries

25g cherries (stones removed)

2 tablespoons golden syrup

75g butter

50g dark chocolate

1 Crush (not too finely)
rolling pin — biscuits

2 oats — all fruit — wooden spoon — crushed biscuits

3 chocolate — syrup — butter — Melt and stir — pan — gentle heat

4 melted butter, chocolate and syrup — biscuit and fruit mixture

5 mixture — Press — baking tray

6 fridge — 30 minutes to 1 hour

7 knife — cut into squares

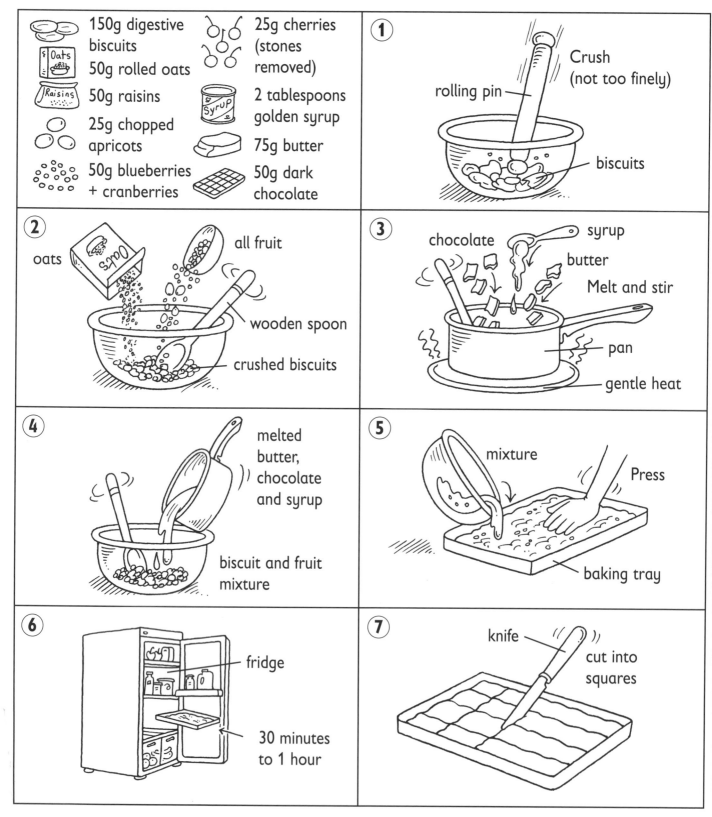

Teachers' note Give the children time to look at the pictures to find out how to make the chocolate slice, then ask them to take turns with a partner, telling him or her what to do. They could actually make the chocolate slice as they do so. Ask them to point out if their partner says anything that does not sound like an instruction.

166

A Lesson for Every Day
Literacy
7–8 Years
© A&C Black

No-cook chocolate slice: 2

• Write the recipe for no-cook chocolate slice.

No-cook chocolate slice

Ingredients

150g digestive biscuits _____   _____

_____   _____

_____   _____

_____

1 Crush the biscuits with _____

_____

2 Mix _____

_____

3 Cut _____

_____

4 _____

_____

5 _____

6 _____

7 _____

NOW TRY THIS!

• **Test the instructions .**
• **Change them if you need to.**

Teachers' note The children first need to have completed 'No-cook chocolate slice: 1'. They could refer to the picture recipe to help them to write this recipe using words only.

A Lesson for Every Day
Literacy
7–8 Years
© A&C Black

Fact-finder

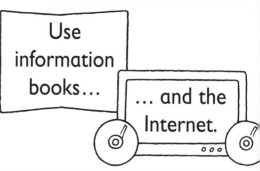

- **Write six** facts **about teeth.**
- **Write where you found each fact.**
- **Check each fact in another book, CD, DVD or website.**

Fact	Where I found it	Where I checked it

NOW TRY THIS!

- **Make an information page about teeth.**

Work with a group.

Teachers' note Ask the children about the difference between fact and fiction. Explain why it is useful to make a note of where information was found (so that it can easily be checked later or so that the same source can be used to find out more).

A Lesson for Every Day
Literacy
7–8 Years
© A&C Black

Now wash your hands

- **Plan an** `information` **poster for younger children.**
- **List three times when they should wash their hands.**
- **Say why.**

Use
information
books.

Use
information
websites.

You should wash your hands…

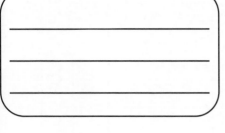
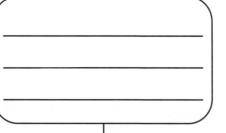
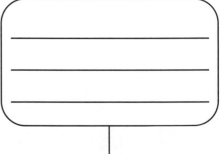

because…

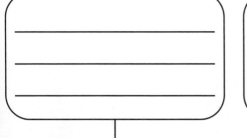
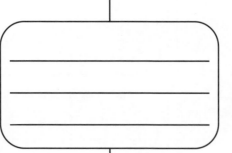
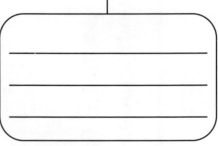

If you do not…

Write the facts
you found.

_____

_____

_____

NOW TRY THIS!

- **Make your poster.**

Use a
computer.

Teachers' note The children could first discuss the topic with their group and make a list of the times when it is important to wash their hands. Point out that they are going to write this information for younger children and that they should think about how to write the information in simple language and how pictures might help.

A Lesson for Every Day
Literacy
7–8 Years
© A&C Black

School dinners

- **Find out what is good about school dinners.**
- **Write four [facts] and why they are good.**

Where I found out	Fact	Why it is good

NOW TRY THIS!

- Write an [information] sheet for parents about school dinners.

Teachers' note Set the children the task of finding facts about school meals. Stress that they are not going to write what they think about the meals (their opinions) but facts that can be checked and, so that the facts can be checked, they should make a note of where they found them. These could be about menu choice, recipes, regulations, cost, nutrition and so on.

A Lesson for Every Day
Literacy
7–8 Years
© A&C Black

School dinners cards

Take photographs of three school dinners.

Write captions that give information.

Make up a song about school dinners.

Make them sound appetising.

Write a quiz about school dinners.

Give information.

Write a poem about school dinners.

Make them sound delicious.

Write a glossary of school dinner ingredients.

Write a sentence about each ingredient.

Design a menu.

Write today's school dinner on it. Add pictures.

Write a recipe for a school dinner.

List the ingredients. Write step-by-step instructions.

Write a script for a short play about school dinner time.

Act the play with your group.

Write a fable that shows school dinners to be good.

The characters could be people or animals.

Teachers' note Cut out the cards, turn them face down and ask each group to take one. Tell the children that their task is to present facts about school dinners in a way that makes children want to eat them. They should follow the instructions on their card.

A Lesson for Every Day
Literacy
7-8 Years
© A&C Black

Bedtime

Anna is three years old.
She does not want to go to bed.
- **Write what her mother and father might say.**

Write facts.
Give reasons.

I don't want to go to bed.

You must go to bed or else you will _____

_____

_____

I'm not tired.

I don't like sleeping.

If you don't sleep

_____

_____

_____

Anna

You're not going to bed yet. It's not fair.

_____

_____

_____

_____

_____

NOW TRY THIS!

- **Act this scene with a friend.**
- **Add more dialogue.**

Teachers' note Ask the children if they have ever argued with a parent about bedtime and, if so, what they said and what their parents said. Set them the challenge of writing a mother's replies to a three-year-old who does not want to go to bed. They could role-play the scene before writing it.

A Lesson for Every Day
Literacy
7-8 Years
© A&C Black

Wonderful worms

Jess wants to keep some worms to recycle her family's food scraps to make compost. Her dad does not like the idea.

- Write what Jess might say.

Jess

Jess's dad

We don't have enough space to keep a wormery.

We don't need compost because we only have a tiny garden.

The wormery might smell.

I would end up doing all the work of looking after the worms.

NOW TRY THIS!

- Act this with a friend.
- Write a play script for the scene.

Teachers' note Ask the children to read Jess's father's reasons for not having a wormery, to find out some facts about keeping worms (see the notes on the activity on page 20) and to use these to help them to write Jess's replies, which should include facts.

A Lesson for Every Day
Literacy
7–8 Years
© A&C Black

Time sentences

- **Read the sentences.**
- **Add information about time.**
- **Read the new sentences with a friend.**

Use the time-bank.

1 I found my purse _____ .

2 _____ I had seen a stranger in the street.

3 _____ I thought there was something odd about him.

4 We would have to get home _____ .

5 She said she would phone me _____ .

6 The police had warned us about bike thieves

_____ .

7 We saw Orion and other star groups _____ .

8 We were glad to see our friends again _____ .

Time-bank

at first	earlier that morning
later in the evening	before it got dark
only a few days earlier	after the summer holidays
that night	later that day

NOW TRY THIS!

- **Write time sentences using these.**

a few weeks later	in the middle of the night

Teachers' note Read the first example with the children and discuss the purpose of the words *I found* and *my purse*. *I found* says what people did and *my purse* says what they did it to. Tell them that they are going to write a word or words in the gap to say when this happened. Ask them to choose the most appropriate word/s from the time-bank.

A Lesson for Every Day
Literacy
7-8 Years
© A&C Black

Place to place

Where might it have happened?
- **Write in the gaps.**
- **Read the sentences.**

Use the place-bank.

1 They could see a ship _____.

2 _____ a plume of smoke rose from the chimney of a farmhouse.

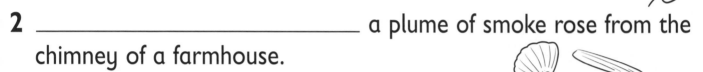

3 _____ two boys were picking up shells.

4 _____ her mother would be waiting.

5 It would be less windy _____.

6 He could hear the sound of a chainsaw cutting wood _____.

7 Lights glittered _____.

8 She spotted a heron wading _____.

Place-bank

in the distant village	down on the beach
across the valley	in the forest
at the edge of the pond	far out at sea
on the other side of the wall	back at home

NOW TRY THIS!

- **Write time sentences using these.**

on the other side	in the distance

Teachers' note Read the first example with the children and discuss the purpose of the words *They could see* and *a ship. They could see* says what people did and *a ship* says what they did it to. Tell them that they are going to write a word or words in the gap to say where this happened. Ask them to choose the most appropriate word/s from the place-bank.

A Lesson for Every Day
Literacy
7–8 Years
© A&C Black

Dark

- **Read the poem with your group.**
- **Make notes about how to recite it.**
- **Underline parts to help.**

> How should your voice sound? Think about the atmosphere.

The Dark Wood

In the dark, dark wood, there was
a dark, dark house,
And in that dark, dark house, there was
a dark, dark room,
And in that dark, dark room, there was
a dark, dark cupboard,
And in that dark, dark cupboard, there was
a dark, dark shelf,
And on that dark, dark shelf there was
a dark, dark box,
And in that dark, dark box, there was a

GHOST!

Anon

Notes

Atmosphere _____
_____

Quiet parts _____
_____

Getting louder _____
_____

Very loud _____
_____

Slow parts _____
_____

Getting faster _____
_____

Pauses _____
_____

NOW TRY THIS!

- **Make up your own version of the poem.**

> Work with your group. Make sure that everyone joins in. Ask others for ideas. Ask what they think.

Teachers' note The children could begin by reading the poem to themselves or with a partner. Pair low-attaining readers with those who can read without difficulty or with one another for mutual support. They can then talk to their groups about the atmosphere of the poem and how to read it. They could use tape recorders or MP3 players to record and replay their readings for evaluating and changing.

A Lesson for Every Day
Literacy
7-8 Years
© A&C Black

The Train

- **Look at the poem with your group.**
- **Underline the main story in red and the repeated words in green.**
- **Now split into two smaller groups – Group A and Group B.**
- **Complete the notes about how to recite the poem.**
- **Perform the poem.**

Stay in your smaller groups for the performance.

The Train

The train goes running along the line.

Jicketty-can, jicketty-can.

I wish it were mine, I wish it were mine.

Jicketty-can, jicketty-can.

The engine driver stands in front,

He makes it run, he makes it shunt.

Out of town,

Out of town,

Over hill,

Over the down,

Under the bridge,

Across the lea,

Over the ridge

And down by the sea,

With a jicketty-can, jicketty-can,

Jicketty- jicketty-jicketty-can,

Jicketty-can, jicketty-can.

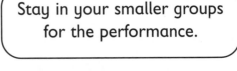

Clive Sansom

Group A

Say the lines underlined in red.

The rhythm sounds like

_____

Make it louder/quieter than Group B.

Group B

Keep repeating these words:

_____

The rhythm sounds like

_____

Make it louder/quieter than Group A.

Other notes

_____

_____

_____

_____

Teachers' note The children could start by reading the second line several times. What do the rhythm and sound remind them of? Half of each group should repeat this while the others read the poem. Encourage them to experiment with changing the speed and volume. They could 'fade out' at the end to suggest the train disappearing into the distance.

A Lesson for Every Day
Literacy
7–8 Years
© A&C Black

De Bottleman

- **Read the poem.**
- **Make notes about how to recite it. The notes have been started for you.**

Work with a partner.

De Bottleman

Bottles! Bottles!
Bottles I buy.

Hear de bottleman cry

Long bottles
Short bottles
Fat bottles
Thin bottles

Bottles! Bottles!
Bottles I buy

Hear de bottleman cry

Search low search high.

I buy dem wet
I buy dem dry

Run with a bottle
to de bottleman cart
when yuh hear de bottleman cry

Bottles! Bottles!
Bottles I buy.

John Agard

Call out loudly

Say it quickly and quietly

NOW TRY THIS!

- **Recite the poem to another pair.**
- **Mark anything you need to read differently.**

178

Teachers' note Model how to read the bottleman's cry (as if calling out from the street to people indoors). Help the children distinguish between what he calls out and how it is described, and discuss how punctuation could help. The children could mark commas, full stops and speech marks. Discuss why some of the words are not spelled as the children might expect: *de* (the), *yuh* (you).

A Lesson for Every Day
Literacy
7–8 Years
© A&C Black

This is the greatest!

- **Work in a large group.**

  ☆ Cut out the cards.

  ☆ Put them in a pile, face down.

  ☆ Each pick up a card.

  ☆ Take turns to explain why this object is the most important.

> A diamond is the most important because...

 a diamond	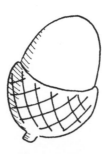 an acorn	 a light bulb
 a cloud	 a fire	 a pencil
 the moon	 a spade	 a bag of flour

NOW TRY THIS!

- **Take a vote to decide which object is the most important.**

Teachers' note Split the class into groups of up to nine and give each group two copies of this page. They should keep one copy intact to remind them of the objects in the collection. Give the children a few minutes to think about what they can say to show how important the object on their card is. They could make notes to help them.

A Lesson for Every Day
Literacy
7–8 Years
© A&C Black

Actions speak louder

- ## Work with a partner.
- ## Cut out the cards.
- ## Match the characters to the descriptions.

Characters

Descriptions

This man has just got the baby to sleep and is tiptoeing out of the room.	This girl has just heard that she has got top grades in her tests.
This boy has been hit and called names by a group of children from his school. He had thought some of them were his friends.	This girl wants her mum to let her stay up late to watch a film on television. She says that all her friends are going to watch it and she will be the only one not allowed.
This keen gardener is telling off his neighbour's children for spoiling his flower bed. He has spent a lot of time caring for his flower bed.	This grandmother has just got off the train and is being met by her grandchildren.

NOW TRY THIS!

- ## Take turns to mime one of the actions in the pictures. Your partner has to guess which it is.

180

Teachers' note You could introduce this by showing the children a video of a television drama with the sound turned off. Ask them what feelings the characters are showing, and how they can tell. Focus on the characters' stance and posture, how they move their arms, the angle of their heads and so on.

A Lesson for Every Day
Literacy
7–8 Years
© A&C Black

Face to face

Faces can show feelings.

- Draw lines to match the characters to the way they are feeling.

 amused

shocked

happy

sad

 surprised

excited

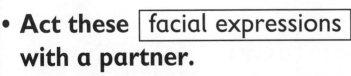

Work with a partner.

- **Act these** facial expressions **with a partner.**
  Tick the feelings your partner shows as well.

NOW TRY THIS!

- **Choose three of the feelings. Use them in a role-play with your partner.**

Teachers' note This activity could be introduced by showing a video of cartoons, which exaggerate gestures and facial expressions. Pause the video and ask the children to mimic some of the facial expressions of the characters. Discuss the feelings being portrayed. Pairs who complete the extension activity can perform their role-plays for others to comment on how well they showed the feelings.

A Lesson for Every Day
Literacy
7–8 Years
© A&C Black

Sounds the same

- **Write the words in the gaps.**
- **Read the sentences.**

> The words sound the same. They are boxed:homophones. But they have different spellings and different meanings.

The roof of the shed _____ when it rains.   leeks

My mum grows prize-winning _____ in her allotment.   leaks

The farmer drove a _____ of cattle down the lane.   herd

We _____ a crash but it was just Dad dropping the plates.   heard

---

The fairytale _____ was paved with gold.   road

She _____ her bike along the golden _____ .   rode   road

There was a thick, swirling _____ over the mountains.   missed

I ran to the bus stop but I _____ the bus.   mist

Jack made a cake with _____, butter, eggs and sugar.   flour

Meere saw a big yellow _____ growing in the garden.   flower

_____ mum lifted a heavy _____ .   hour   weight

They had to _____ an _____ for the train.   our   wait

NOW TRY THIS!

- **Write sentences using homophones that mean these.**

underground part of a plant
+ the way to go somewhere

looks hard + a long set of steps

a man or a boy + the post

Teachers' note The children could use a dictionary to check the meanings of the words. Encourage them to use clues from the context: in the fourth example, they should notice that *missed* is clearly a verb in the second sentence and so should have an -ed suffix for the past tense.

A Lesson for Every Day
Literacy
7–8 Years
© A&C Black

Compound word dominoes: 1

over	slide	bare	land	thread	under
time	worm	take	side	look	band
out	hole	back	key	ball	book
man	craft	line	show	work	wild
wood	lamp	hand	head	back	life
stand	business	way	mill	main	back
stone	down	wind	out	fire	foot
water	rail	woman	fall	time	power

Teachers' note Cut along the dotted lines only, to create 48 dominoes. A child deals out the dominoes in a group of four. The first player (left of the dealer) places a domino face up. The next player tries to place a domino to join either end to make a compound word, e.g. *landslide*. The word already laid can form the first or the last part of the new word.

A Lesson for Every Day
Literacy
7–8 Years
© A&C Black

Compound word dominoes: 2

suit	light	beat	wind	ground	green
play	line	beat	high	boy	boat
sand	ship	light	hood	age	spot
work	ever	girl	off	house	how
friend	sand	life	quick	any	paper
home	back	bag	screen	wreck	owner
lift	pipe	date	bank	floor	up
table	note	turn	shop	book	cloth

Teachers' note Cut along the dotted lines only, to create 48 dominoes. A child deals out the dominoes in a group of four. The first player (left of the dealer) places a domino face up. The next player tries to place a domino to join either end to make a compound word: e.g. *lighthouse*. The word already laid can form the first or the last part of the new word.

A Lesson for Every Day
Literacy
7–8 Years
© A&C Black

All in a day's work

- **Match the songs to the work.**
- **Read or sing the songs as you mime the work or actions.**

Think about the rhythm.

Volga boatmen's song ①

Now we fell the stout birch tree,
Now we pull hard: one, two, three.
Ay-da, da, ay-da!
Ay-da, da, ay-da!
Now we fell the stout birch tree
Yo, heave ho!
Hey, hey, let's heave a-long the way
to the sun we sing our song
Yo, heave ho! Yo, heave ho!

Dark as the dungeon ②

It's dark as the dungeon and damp as the dew,
Where danger is double and pleasures are few,
Where the rain never falls and the sun never shines
It's dark as a dungeon way down in the mine.

Casey Jones ③

Casey Jones mounted to his cabin,
Casey Jones with his orders in his hand
Casey Jones mounted to his cabin,
And he took his farewell trip to that promised land.

Hoe, Emma, Hoe ④

Caller: Hoe, Emma, Hoe,
You turn around dig a hole in the ground,
Hoe, Emma, Hoe.
Chorus: Hoe, Emma, Hoe…
Caller: Emma, you from the country.
Chorus: Hoe, Emma, Hoe...

Leave her, Johnny, leave her! ⑤

Leave her, Johnny, leave her!
I thought I heard, the old man say,
Leave her, Johnny, leave her!
You can go ashore and draw your pay,
It's time for us to leave her!

 Mining coal

☐ Rowing a boat

 Driving an engine

☐ Digging the land

 Sailors hauling in ropes

Teachers' note Explain that many workers have made up songs to take their minds off boring, repetitive or strenuous work or to help them keep to a rhythm such as rowing, digging or hauling on a rope. If possible, let them listen to the songs being sung.

A Lesson for Every Day
Literacy
7–8 Years
© A&C Black

Elimination poem

- **Plan how to perform this poem with a group.**
- **Write and draw your plan.**

Think about the changes that can be seen and heard.

Ten Tall Oaktrees

Ten tall oaktrees,
Standing in a line,
"Warships," cried King Henry,
Then there were nine.

Nine tall oaktrees,
Growing strong and straight,
"Charcoal," breathed the furnace,
Then there were eight.

Eight tall oaktrees,
Reaching towards heaven,
"Sizzle," spoke the lightning,
Then there were seven.

Seven tall oaktrees,
Branches, leaves and sticks,
"Firewood," smiled the merchant,
Then there were six.

Six tall oaktrees,
Glad to be alive,
"Barrels," boomed the brewery,
Then there were five.

Five tall oaktrees,
Suddenly a roar,
"Gangway," screamed the west wind,
Then there were four.

Four tall oaktrees,
Sighing like the sea,
"Floorboards," beamed the builder,
Then there were three.

Three tall oaktrees,
Groaning as trees do,
"Unsafe," claimed the council,
Then there were two.

Two tall oaktrees,
Spreading in the sun,
"Progress," snarled the by-pass,
Then there was one.

One tall oaktree,
Wishing it could run,
"Nuisance," grumped the farmer,
Then there were none.

No tall oaktrees,
Search the fields in vain:
Only empty skylines
And the cold, grey rain.

By Richard Edwards

NOW TRY THIS!

- **Be a director.**
- **Make a list to say who will do what in your performance.**

Teachers' note Ask the children to read the poem to themselves and discuss what happens to the oak woods. Encourage them to talk about ways of performing it to communicate the idea of the trees going, one by one.

A Lesson for Every Day
Literacy
7–8 Years
© A&C Black

Packing to go

- **Imagine your family had to leave your home in a hurry. What would you take with you? Why?**
- **Make notes on the chart.**

Apart from clothes, you can take:
a book, a toy or game and one other thing.

My choices	Reasons
Book	
Toy or game	
Other	

- **Explain your choices to the rest of the group.**

NOW TRY THIS!

- **What if a parent or carer wanted to stop you taking these things? Role-play what they might say and what you would say.**

Work with a partner.

Teachers' note First read some accounts of families who have had to flee their homes with a limited amount of luggage, such as *When Hitler Stole Pink Rabbit* by Judith Kerr. Draw out that these people could take only the most important things with them. The children could discuss in pairs which objects are important to them. (Tell them that all family members and pets will be taken.)

A Lesson for Every Day
Literacy
7–8 Years
© A&C Black

Short story

- **Rewrite the words in bold type.**
- **Use an** boxed[apostrophe] **to make their short forms.**

Apostrophes show where letters have been missed out.

Examples: he is → he's

cannot → can't

"**What is** <u>What's</u> that **you are** _____ wearing, Salim?" asked Sally.

"**It is** _____ my new space suit," answered Salim.

"**We are** _____ going to Mars for our holiday."

"**I would** _____ love to go there," said Sally.

"**You will** _____ be able to see the Red Dust Park.

I have _____ asked my dad if we can go there but he says that **we shall** _____ just go to the Moon again.

He **cannot** _____ afford the fares."

"**You are** _____ lucky," said Salim. "You **do not** _____ need to have all the injections."

"**That is** _____ true," replied Sally. "**There is** _____ quite a lot to do on the Moon, too. You **do not** _____ get bored there."

The next day Salim told Sally that he **would not** _____ be going to the Moon for his holidays, after all.

"Dad **could not** _____ get any spacecraft tickets," he said. "They were all booked up for the school holidays and he **will not** _____ let us stay off school."

NOW TRY THIS!

- **Write sentences using the short forms of these.**

  boxed[we will not]   boxed[I might not]   boxed[they have]

Teachers' note Introduce this by saying some sentences without using contractions and ask the children what sounds unusual: for example, *I cannot find my key, I do not remember where I left it.* Write up the contractions above their full versions and ask the children to explain how they were formed.

A Lesson for Every Day
Literacy
7-8 Years
© A&C Black

Shorten it

- **Write the** | contraction |.
- **Write how you made this.**

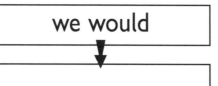

A contraction is when two words are joined and shortened.

they are	we would	could not
↓	↓	↓
they're		

I joined <u>they</u> and <u>are</u>. I left out <u>a</u> and put an apostrophe in its place.	I joined _____ and _____. I left out _____ and _____ _____ _____ _____	I joined _____ and _____. I left out _____ and _____ _____ _____ _____

- **Write instructions for making contractions.**

1. _____

2. _____

3. _____

NOW TRY THIS!

- **Write a contraction that is an exception to the rules.**
- **Tell a friend why you think this is.**

Teachers' note The children should first have completed 'Short story'. Point out that the contractions on this page are formed when two words are joined and letters missed out. Ask them how they can tell where the missing letters were.

A Lesson for Every Day
Literacy
7-8 Years
© A&C Black

Fun shapes

- ## What do these say?
- ## Write the words.

bbbbbbbbbbbbbb
bbbbbbbbbb
b
b b bbbbbbbbbbbb
b bbbbbbbbbb
b bbbbbbbbbbbb
b bbbbbbbbbb
b bbbbbbbbbbbbb
b bbbbb bbbb
b b b

dddddddd
dddddddd
ddd
ddd
ddd
dddddddd
dddddd

d
dddddd
dddddddddd
dddddddddddd
d

NOW TRY THIS!

- ## Use letters to write these words as shapes.

before   seagull   army

Teachers' note Introduce the idea of playing with the appearance of words in order to say something in a clever way. Show them other examples. You could complete the first example with the children to show what is meant.

A Lesson for Every Day
Literacy
7–8 Years
© A&C Black

Penguin

- **Watch a recording of penguins walking.**
- **Move as if you are a penguin.**
- **On the notepad write words for how they move.**

Notepad

_____

_____

_____

_____

_____

_____

- **Choose the best words.**
- **Write them in a poem about penguins.**

Think about rhythm.

Do not try to make rhymes.

Your poem need not have sentences.

_____

_____

_____

_____

_____

_____

NOW TRY THIS!

- **Read your poem aloud with a friend.**
- **Make notes about how to improve it.**

Teachers' note Several recordings of penguins walking can be found on the International Bird Collection website at www.hbw.com/ibc. Some useful words and phrases to communicate the waddling movement of penguins are: _flopping, flapping, webbed-feet waddling, flip-flap of feet, straight-backed, wings like flippers, yellow beaks like noses, pointing._

A Lesson for Every Day
Literacy
7–8 Years
© A&C Black

Word shapes

- **Write the words so that their shapes show their meanings.**

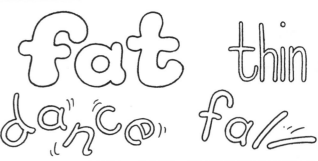

wriggle	smile	look
moon	climb	steps
stretch	squash	mountain

NOW TRY THIS!

- **Write four other words in shapes that show their meanings.**

Teachers' note The children could first draw the shape of the meaning of each word and then write the word on it.

A Lesson for Every Day
Literacy
7-8 Years
© A&C Black

Flat fish and wiggly worms

- **List some words to:**
  - describe each animal
  - say how it moves.
- **Write** [calligrams] **on the shapes.**

Use alliteration.

Write in colour.

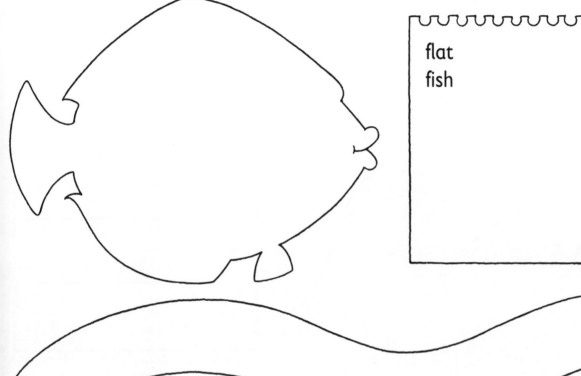

flat
fish

wiggly
worm

NOW TRY THIS!

- **Draw and write calligrams about:**

  [a seal]   [a crab]

Teachers' note Ask the children first to list some words to describe the animal and how it moves. They can then combine these to form phrases or sentences and write them in the form of a poem on the animal outline.

A Lesson for Every Day
Literacy
7–8 Years
© A&C Black

Waterfall

- **Watch a recording of a waterfall.**
- **Write notes about:**
  - **– the sounds**
  - **– the colours**
  - **– the movements**
  - **– the atmosphere.**
- **Write a poem to show the** shape **of the waterfall.**

Write on the lines.

Notes

_____
_____
_____
_____
_____
_____
_____
_____
_____
_____
_____
_____
_____
_____
_____
_____
_____

NOW TRY THIS!

- **Draw some lines for a poem about dancing.**

Teachers' note Several websites showing recordings of waterfalls can be found from a search (enter video + waterfall): for example, www.metacafe.com, www.leechvideo.com/tag/Waterfall and www.ncwaterfalls.com. Link this with work on verbs, adjectives and adverbs.

A Lesson for Every Day
Literacy
7–8 Years
© A&C Black

- **Make notes for a** shape poem **about a sunflower.**
- **Write your poem on the shape.**

Use adjectives and similes.

Think about . . .   . . . colour . . .   . . . life cycle . . .

Notes

dying like the setting sun

blazing yellow

NOW TRY THIS!

- **Read your poem with a friend.**
- **See if you can think of better words to use.**

Teachers' note If possible provide a real sunflower for the children to observe. They could compare it with another, completely different flower, such as a bluebell, clover, geranium or snowdrop. Ask them what it reminds them of, and why. Focus on why it is so named and help the children to write comparisons with the sun (rising and setting, shining, blazing and so on).

A Lesson for Every Day
Literacy
7–8 Years
© A&C Black

A sentence in any shape

- **Write sentences about these:**

  | a snake | a tower | a tree |

- **Practise on scrap paper.**
- **Choose a shape to write each sentence on.**

NOW TRY THIS!

- **Draw three other shapes to write sentences on.**
- **Give them to a friend to write one.**

Teachers' note Encourage children to use scrap paper for writing words to describe the appearance of the subject and how it affects people, animals or its surroundings. These could include expressive verbs to create an impression of how the subject moves or how it exists: for example, *nestles, towers, looms, slithers, glides.*

A Lesson for Every Day
Literacy
7–8 Years
© A&C Black

You're joking!

- **Read the first joke with a partner.**
- **Write notes to help you to read the other jokes.**
- **Read the other jokes with your partner.**

Talk about how the notes helped.

Knock, knock.

Who's there?

Amos.

Amos who?

A mosquito!

Patient: Doctor, doctor –

I think I'm invisible.

Can you help me?

Doctor: Who said that?

What did the man say when his son swallowed a harmonica?

I'm glad he doesn't play the piano.

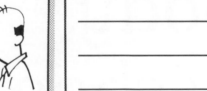

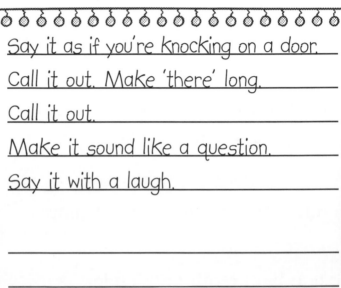

Say it as if you're knocking on a door.

Call it out. Make 'there' long.

Call it out.

Make it sound like a question.

Say it with a laugh.

_____

_____

_____

_____

_____

_____

_____

_____

NOW TRY THIS!

- **Write another joke.**
- **Write notes on how to read it.**
- **Tell the joke to your group.**

Work with a partner.

Teachers' note Ask the children to cover the notepad, then read the first joke with a partner. Then they should read the notes together. Discuss what they mean: how they can sound as if they are knocking (they could knock on a table top) and how they should call out to the person at the door. They should then read the other jokes and make notes on how to deliver them.

A Lesson for Every Day
Literacy
7–8 Years
© A&C Black

How loud?

- **Plan how to read the poem aloud with a partner.**
- **Colour the 'loudness scale' for each part.**
- **Read the poem aloud with your friend.**

Talk about how the notes helped.

Louder!

Loudness scale

OK, Andrew, nice and clearly – off you go.

1	2	3	4	5	6

Welcome everybody to our school concert...

1	2	3	4	5	6

Louder, please, Andrew. Mums and dads won't hear you at the back, will they?

1	2	3	4	5	6

Welcome everybody to our school concert...

1	2	3	4	5	6

Louder, Andrew. You're not trying.

Pro – ject – your – voice.

1	2	3	4	5	6

Take a big breath and louder!

Welcome everybody to our school concert...

1	2	3	4	5	6

For goodness sake, Andrew. LOUDER! LOUDER!

1	2	3	4	5	6

Welcome everybody to our school concert...

1	2	3	4	5	6

Key

1 very quiet

2 quiet

3 fairly quiet

4 normal

5 loud

6 very loud

Now, Andrew, there's no need to be silly.

Roger Stevens

Teachers' note Help the children to understand the 'loudness scale': 1 whisper, 2 loud whisper, 3 low voice, 4 normal voice, 5 raised voice, 6 shout. Practise these before they read the poem aloud. Refer to this scale in other speaking situations: they should consider the size of the audience, how far away they are and other sounds that might make their voices hard to hear.

A Lesson for Every Day
Literacy
7–8 Years
© A&C Black

Tell me more

- **Work with a partner.**
- **Ask your partner this question:**

> What should you do if you see a friend stealing?

- **Make notes about what your partner says.**
  Ask more questions to keep your partner talking.

You should _____

_____

because _____

> Why...?

_____

_____

> How...?

_____

_____

_____

> What...?

_____

_____

NOW TRY THIS!

- **Explain your partner's view to the group.**

Teachers' note Explain that in this activity the children are going to encourage a partner to talk about his or her views by listening and answering questions. One child should find out the other's views, then they should swap roles. Remind them about good listening skills (see notes on the activity on page 22). Point out the question words in the speech bubbles and how these are useful for finding information during conversations.

A Lesson for Every Day
Literacy
7–8 Years
© A&C Black

Words ending le

- ## Write le words in the gaps.

A _____ can be made of glass or plastic.

le word-bank

ankle	pebble
apple	staple
bottle	table
bugle	wobble
jungle	wrinkle

A _____ is a hot damp forest.

A _____ is a smooth, rounded stone.

An _____ is a red or green fruit.

We eat at the _____.

Your _____ is the joint between your leg and your foot.

You can fasten papers with a _____.

A _____ is a crease in skin or cloth.

A _____ is a musical instrument.

_____ means to shake.

NOW TRY THIS!

- ## Write le words that mean:

| mutter | twice as much | a horse's home |

Teachers' note Ask the children to write a few words with the **-le** ending, perhaps using phoneme frames, on wipe-off boards. Invite feedback, discuss discrepancies and say why any 'reasonable' wrong ones, such as **-el**, **-al** or **-il**, are good attempts.

A Lesson for Every Day
Literacy
7-8 Years
© A&C Black

Words ending el

- **Write** el **words in the gaps.**

A _____ is a fish.

el word-bank

bagel	mackerel
barrel	novel
diesel	towel
easel	trowel
jewel	vowel

You can paint on an _____.

_____ is a type of oil.

A _____ is a story.

A _____ is a garden tool.

Beer is kept in a _____.

The letter a is a _____.

I dried my hands on a _____.

A ruby is a _____.

A _____ is a type of bread.

NOW TRY THIS!

- **Write** el **words that mean:**

an animal with a hump	a package

little bits of stone used on paths

a dog that is a mixture of breeds

Teachers' note First complete 'Words ending -le'. Ask the children to write a few words with the **-el** ending, perhaps using phoneme frames, on wipe-off boards. Invite feedback, discuss discrepancies and say why any 'reasonable' wrong ones, such as **-le**, **-al** or **-il**, are good attempts.

A Lesson for Every Day
Literacy
7-8 Years
© A&C Black

Words ending al

- **Write** al **words in the gaps.**

al **word-bank**

bridal	local
cathedral	musical
equal	royal
hospital	sandal
legal	spiral

_____ means allowed by law.

_____ means tuneful.

Doctors and nurses work in a _____.

= _____ means the same as.

The queen is head of the _____ family.

A _____ is an open shoe.

A _____ is an important church.

A snail's shell has a _____ shape.

_____ means near where we live.

_____ means concerning a bride.

NOW TRY THIS!

- **Write** al **words that mean:**

on a coast	in the post

concerning machines

Teachers' note First complete 'Words ending -le' and 'Words ending -el'. Ask the children to write a few words with the **-al** ending, perhaps using phoneme frames, on wipe-off boards. Invite feedback, discuss discrepancies and say why any 'reasonable' wrong ones, such as **-le**, **-el** or **-il**, are good attempts.

A Lesson for Every Day
Literacy
7–8 Years
© A&C Black

il wordsearch

- **Loop nine** il **words in the wordsearch.**
- **List them on the notepad below.**
  One is done for you.

> The word can go from left to right or downwards.

V	B	C	M	I	N	S	T	E	N	C	I	L	V	X	M
R	H	I	I	K	K	D	E	V	I	L	M	B	O	P	P
U	U	V	Z	B	N	M	Z	P	W	Q	U	Y	S	F	G
P	L	K	P	E	N	C	I	L	K	L	N	N	N	L	D
B	C	J	W	E	R	T	T	Y	U	I	O	P	G	E	A
F	O	S	S	I	L	D	O	S	F	G	H	J	E	N	K
L	U	Z	X	C	V	B	N	M	Q	W	R	T	R	T	R
Y	N	U	I	O	P	P	S	S	A	A	D	D	B	I	F
G	C	H	J	K	L	L	I	Z	X	P	E	R	I	L	C
C	I	V	V	B	N	M	L	M	M	Q	Q	W	L	R	T
Y	L	U	U	I	I	O	O	P	P	P	A	S	D	F	F

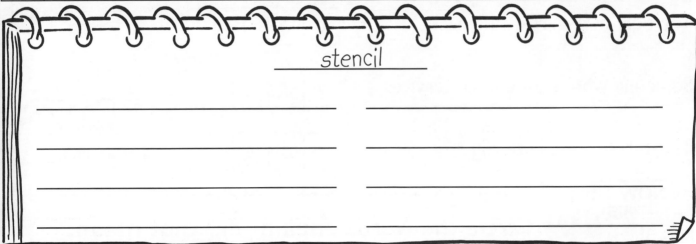

stencil

_____   _____

_____   _____

_____   _____

NOW TRY THIS!

- **Write definitions for three words from the wordsearch.**

Teachers' note First complete 'Words ending -le', 'Words ending -el' and 'Words ending -al'. Ask the children to write a few words with the **-il** ending, perhaps using phoneme frames, on wipe-off boards. Invite feedback, discuss discrepancies and say why any 'reasonable' wrong ones, such as -le, -al or -el, are good attempts.

Think of a word ending `ar`

- **Read the clues.**
- **Write the answers in the phoneme frames.**
- **Read the words.**

> The answers end with the letters `ar`. These can stand for the same phoneme as `er` in <u>mother</u>.

Someone who begs

| b | e | gg | |

A type of tree

| p | o | p | l | |

Use this to sweeten tea or coffee

| s | | | |

Someone who breaks into houses

| b | u | r | | | |

An underground room

| c | e | | |

A large flat tooth

| m | o | | |

The part of a shirt at the neck

| c | o | ll | |

Someone who leads church services

| v | i | c | |

This turns into a butterfly

| c | a | t | | | | | | |

NOW TRY THIS!

- **Circle the words ending `ar` that mean:**

| like a circle | | like a triangle |

| like a rectangle |

| concerning the North or South Pole |

Teachers' note Remind the children of their previous learning about the suffix **-er** and tell them that **-ar** can be added to a few words, such as *beg*, but that usually this ending is not a suffix. Ask the children to write a few words with the **-ar** ending. Point out that most word endings that sound like this are spelled **-er**.

A Lesson for Every Day
Literacy
7-8 Years
© A&C Black

Think of a word ending [re]

- **Read the clues.**
- **Write the answers in the phoneme frames.**
- **Read the words.**

The answers end with the letters [re]. These can stand for the same phoneme as [er] in <u>mother</u>.

The middle
| c | e | n | | |

A thread
| f | i | b | |

A measure of length
| m | e | |

A shorter measure of length
| c | e | n | t | | | | |

An even shorter measure of length
| m | i | ll | i | m | | |

A measure of capacity
| l | i | |

A smaller measure of capacity
| m | i | ll | i | l | |

A type of window or door
| l | o | u | v | |

A measure of an area of land
| a | c | |

A deep, glossy shine
| l | u | s | t | |

**NOW TRY THIS!**

- **Write the words ending [re] that mean:**

| A type of ghost and rhymes with Hector. |
| Thin and sparse and rhymes with eager. |
| A building where you can watch plays. |

Teachers' note First complete 'Think of a word ending -ar'. Tell the children that the ending that sounds like **-ar** can also be spelled **-re**, but that there are very few words like this: show them *tyre* as an example.

A Lesson for Every Day
Literacy
7-8 Years
© A&C Black

Think of a word ending [our]

- **Read the clues.**
- **Write the words ending** [our] **in the phoneme frames.**
- **Read the words.**

The letters [our] can stand for the same phoneme as [er] in <u>mother</u>.

Taste | f | l | a | v | | |

Red is one; so is blue | c | o | l | | |

If you like a joke you have a sense of ____ | h | u | m | | |

Something you hear people talking about | r | u | m | | |

A place where boats can anchor safely | h | ar | | |

Someone who lives near you | n | eigh | | |

You do this for people if you help them | f | a | v | | |

A growth in a human or other animal | t | u | m | | |

Water in the air | v | a | p | | |

Knights wore this in battle | ar | m | | |

NOW TRY THIS!

- **Write words ending** [our] **that come from these words.**

| candid | honest | splendid |

| behave |

 Use a dictionary.

Teachers' note First complete 'Think of a work ending -ar' and 'Think of a word ending -our'. Tell the children that the ending that sounds like **-re** and **-ar** can also be spelled **-our**, but that there are very few words like this: show them *labour* as an example. Ask the children to write the words in sentences and to notice what type of words they are (nouns).

A Lesson for Every Day
Literacy
7–8 Years
© A&C Black

Double trouble

- **Write the missing consonant in each word.**
- **Decide whether it should be single or double.**

t   tt   My mum likes drinking bi____er lemon.

<u>bitter</u>

r   rr   She wants to ma____y him.

s   ss   We ate ice cream for de____ert.

n   nn   A spa____er is a useful tool.

m   mm   You can put a co____a between words in a list.

b   bb   Sam wrote a la____el for Ella's pre____ent.
s   ss

p   pp   The car sto____ed at the tra____ic lights.
f   ff

NOW TRY THIS!

- **Explain why people might spell these words wrongly, with double consonants.**

| panel | camel | cabin | linen | comet |

Teachers' note For revision the children could write words such as *cliff, funny, fuss, fussy, happy, silly*. Read the completed example with them and draw attention to the different phonemes that could be produced. Other examples include *biding/bidding, cuter/cutter, fused/fussed, riding/ridding, robed/robbed.*

A Lesson for Every Day
Literacy
7-8 Years
© A&C Black

Word-builder

• **Add prefixes and suffixes to make new words.**

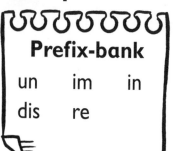

Prefix-bank

| un | im | in |
| dis | re | |

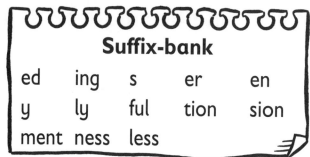

Suffix-bank

ed	ing	s	er	en
y	ly	ful	tion	sion
ment	ness	less		

You might need to change the ending of the word.

Base word   **New words**

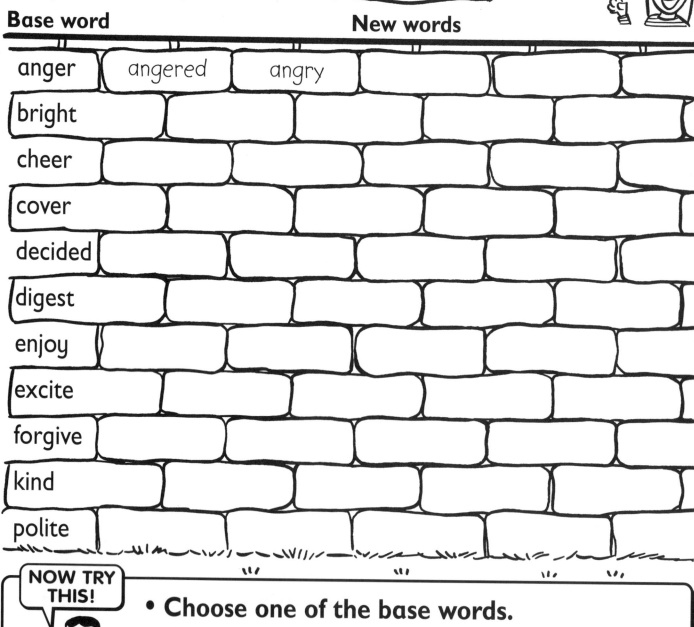

anger	angered	angry			
bright					
cheer					
cover					
decided					
digest					
enjoy					
excite					
forgive					
kind					
polite					

NOW TRY THIS!

• **Choose one of the base words.**
• **Write sentences using the new words you made from it with prefixes and suffixes.**

Teachers' note Model how to complete the first example, by trying out the different prefixes and suffixes and thinking aloud: *Unanger – no I haven't heard that word; imanger – no; inanger – no, that's not a word; disanger – no, that's not a word; reanger – no; angered – yes, that's a word, angering – yes.* Write the new words on the wall and continue.

A Lesson for Every Day
Literacy
7-8 Years
© A&C Black

Odd one out: 1

- **Read the words.**
- **Circle the odd one out in each set.**
- **Tell a friend why it is the odd one out.**

Think about prefixes.

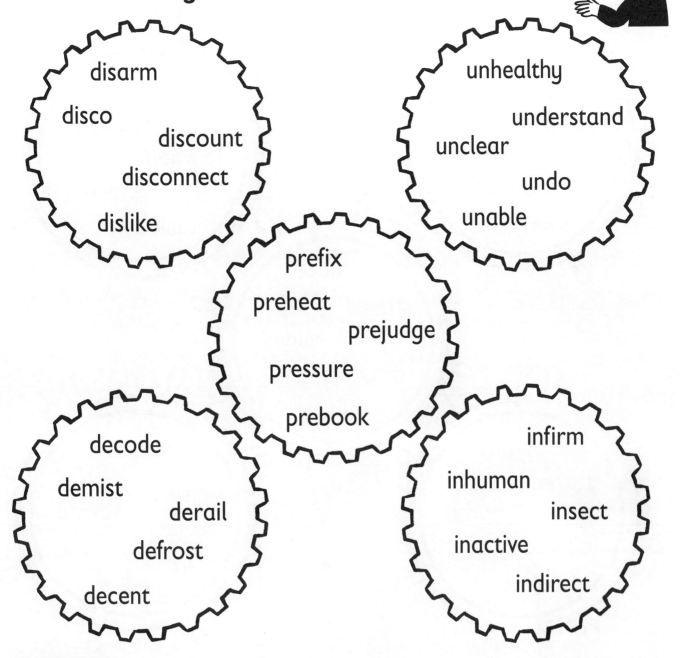

disarm

disco

discount

disconnect

dislike

unhealthy

understand

unclear

undo

unable

prefix

preheat

prejudge

pressure

prebook

decode

demist

derail

defrost

decent

infirm

inhuman

insect

inactive

indirect

NOW TRY THIS!

- **Make another set of five words with an odd one out like these.**
- **Use words that start** de .

Teachers' note How are the words in the first set similar? They all begin with **dis-**, but in some words this is not a prefix. (Ask what is left when they take off **dis-**. Is this a word?) Point out that the **dis-** at the start of *disco* is part of the base word *disc*. Ask them to read the words in each set carefully to check the prefixes.

A Lesson for Every Day
Literacy
7–8 Years
© A&C Black

Odd one out: 2

- **Read the words.**
- **Circle the odd one out in each set.**
- **Tell a friend why it is the odd one out.**

> Think about the past tense.

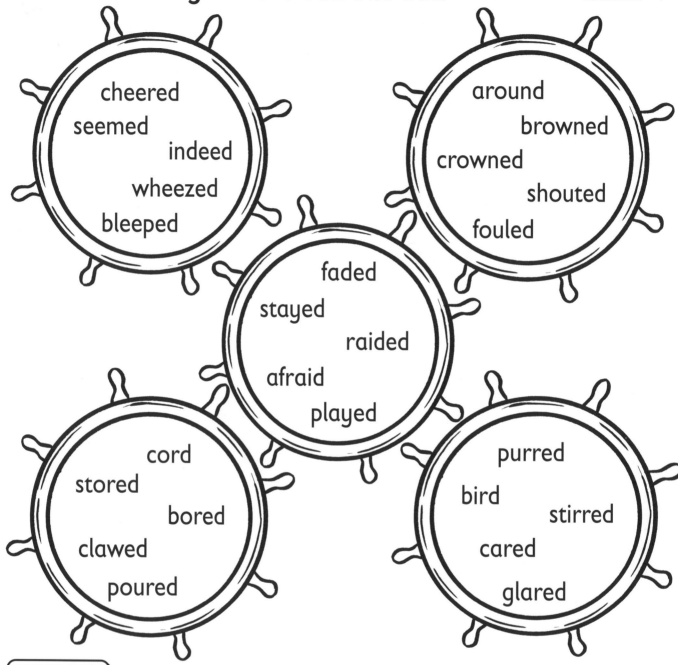

cheered
seemed
indeed
wheezed
bleeped

around
browned
crowned
shouted
fouled

faded
stayed
raided
afraid
played

cord
stored
bored
clawed
poured

purred
bird
stirred
cared
glared

NOW TRY THIS!

- **Make another set of five words with an odd one out like these.**
- **Use words that rhyme with** starred **.**

Teachers' note How are the words in the first set similar? They all end with **d**, but ask the children to look for a word in which this is not part of the past tense suffix **-ed**. Point out that the **ed** at the end of *indeed* is not a past tense suffix. You could also use this page to revise the different graphemes used for the phonemes /ow/, /ai/, /or/ and /ur/.

A Lesson for Every Day
Literacy
7–8 Years
© A&C Black

Flower power

- **On each flower write as many words as you can using the base word.**

import
export
port

side

joy

NOW TRY THIS!

- **Write the longest word you can make from the base word** | form | **.**

Teachers' note Remind the children of the meaning of base word using the first example (*port*). Ask them to suggest other words containing *port*, along with a prefix or suffix, e.g. *deport*, *exported*, *important*, *imported*, *importing*, *porter*, *report*, *reporting*, *support*, *supporting*.

A Lesson for Every Day
Literacy
7-8 Years
© A&C Black

Writing riddles

- **Complete the** `riddles` **and write the answers.**

I have a face

  but no _____ , _____ or _____ .

I have two _____

  but cannot touch you.

I have no mouth

  but can tell you _____ .

Answer _____

I have four _____

  but cannot _____ or _____ .

I have a _____

  but cannot sit down.

My back has no _____

  but it keeps yours _____ .

Answer _____

Some days I go everywhere with you.

Some days I _____ .

I can grow and _____

  when you stay _____ .

The _____ changes my size

  but not yours.

Answer _____

Others see me more than you do.

You see theirs _____ .

There isn't another _____

  and _____ .

Answer _____

NOW TRY THIS!

- **Make up riddles for:**  a car   the sun

---

Teachers' note The children should first have read some riddles. They will probably need help in solving them. Explain that riddles are word puzzles for the reader to answer using different types of clue. They could try solving the ones on this page with a friend and then using them as models for writing their own.

A Lesson for Every Day
Literacy
7–8 Years
© A&C Black

Limerick writer

- **Read the** limerick.
- **Underline the rhyming words.**
- **Complete the other limericks.**

Use a different colour for each rhyme.

Notice the rhythm.

There was an old man of Dundee.
Who went to the mountains to ski.
He slid on his seat
Instead of his feet
And landed on top of a tree.

There was a young lady from Cork

Who _____

_____

_____

Notes

There was an old woman from Leeds

Who _____

_____

_____

Notes

NOW TRY THIS!

- **Write a limerick using the name of another place.**

Work with a friend.

Teachers' note The children could first read some limericks by Edward Lear. Read the example on this page aloud while the children listen and tap the rhythm. Help them to identify the rhyming lines. Before writing the first limerick they could make lists of words that rhyme with *Cork*: for example, *chalk, fork, pork, stalk, stork, talk, walk*.

A Lesson for Every Day
Literacy
7-8 Years
© A&C Black

Sentences in poems

Some poems are not written in sentences **.**
Capital letters might not be only at the
beginnings of sentences.
Full stops might be missing.

Use different colours.

- **Underline the** sentences **.**

From *The Owl and the Pussy Cat*
By Edward Lear

The Owl and the Pussy Cat went to sea
In a beautiful pea-green boat,
They took some honey, and plenty of money,
Wrapped up in a five-pound note.

From *Child's Song in Spring*
By Edith Nesbit

The silver birch is a dainty lady,
She wears a satin gown.
The elm tree makes the old churchyard shady,
She will not live in town.

The English oak is a sturdy fellow,
He gets his green coat late.
The willow is smart in a suit of yellow,
While the brown birch trees wait.

- **Write them on the lines.**

NOW TRY THIS!

- **Talk to a friend about why poems are not always in sentences.**

Put the capital letters and full stops in the correct places.

Teachers' note Point out that poems need not be written in sentences but that many poems
contain sentences. Read the first example with the children so that they can enjoy the rhythm and
humour. Ask them which parts of it are not sentences, and how they can tell. Can they find any
sentences? They can then underline and copy the sentences.

A Lesson for Every Day
Literacy
7–8 Years
© A&C Black

Written evidence
Find out about the past from a range of sources

- What types of information could you find out about the past from an old newspaper?

- Design a front page of a newspaper reporting a school event.

School! New Wildlife area opened

Use this idea to help you.

- List three ways a modern newspaper is different from an old-fashioned one.

Teachers' note Before completing the activity sheet, allow time for the children to examine a selection of different modern newspapers. In small groups children should list what information they contain. Do they all contain the same things? Compare these to old-fashioned newspapers.

16

Photographic evidence
Find out about the past from a range of sources

This photo shows three Victorian children.

Work with a friend.

What can you tell about the children from looking at the photo?

What information can you not find out from the photograph?

What other evidence could a historian use to find out more about the children?

- How are old photos different from modern ones? List your ideas.

Teachers' note The children should work with partners to discuss their observations and complete the activity sheet. Ask them what they can see in the photo. When was the photo taken? How do they know? Can they be more precise? How old are the children? Can they be sure? What other evidence could they use to find out?

Developing History Ages 6–7 © A & C BLACK

17

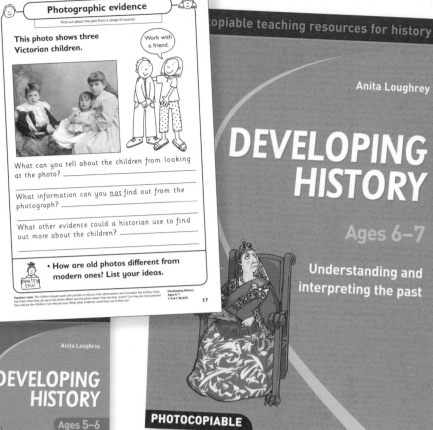

Anita Loughrey

copiable teaching resources for history

DEVELOPING HISTORY

Ages 6–7

Understanding and interpreting the past

PHOTOCOPIABLE

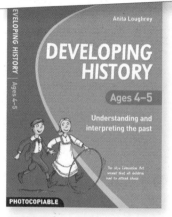

Anita Loughrey

DEVELOPING HISTORY

Ages 4–5

Understanding and interpreting the past

PHOTOCOPIABLE

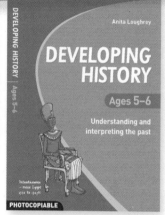

Anita Loughrey

DEVELOPING HISTORY

Ages 5–6

Understanding and interpreting the past

PHOTOCOPIABLE

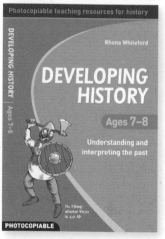

Photocopiable teaching resources for history

Rhona Whiteford

DEVELOPING HISTORY

Ages 7–8

Understanding and interpreting the past

PHOTOCOPIABLE

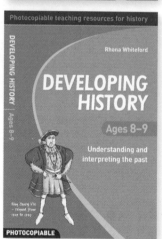

Photocopiable teaching resources for history

Rhona Whiteford

DEVELOPING HISTORY

Ages 8–9

Understanding and interpreting the past

PHOTOCOPIABLE

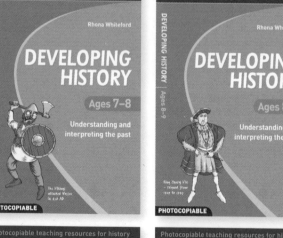

Photocopiable teaching resources for history

Jane Shuter

DEVELOPING HISTORY

Ages 9–10

Understanding and interpreting the past

PHOTOCOPIABLE

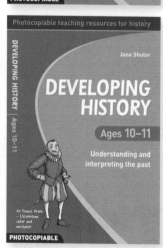

Photocopiable teaching resources for history

Jane Shuter

DEVELOPING HISTORY

Ages 10–11

Understanding and interpreting the past

PHOTOCOPIABLE

Developing History
Understanding and interpreting the past

A series of 7 photocopiable activity books, helping children to understand and interpret the past through learning about the development of Britain, Europe and the world.

Each book includes:

- Rigorous coverage of the National Curriculum programme of study and the QCA scheme of work for history for the Foundation Stage, Key Stage 1 and Key Stage 2.
- Extension activities to reinforce and develop pupils' learning
- Activities that involve ICT, with links to appropriate websites.
- Teachers' notes that give detailed links to other subjects across the curriculum.

For further information contact
A & C Black Customer Services
Telephone 01256 302 692
Fax 01256 812 521
Or visit our website www.acblack.com